Ants
of Surrey

Ants
of Surrey

JOHN PONTIN

SURREY WILDLIFE TRUST

Jacket illustrations
Front cover: *Lasius platythorax* worker tending aphids on apple leaf,
by Andy Callow
Back cover: *Formica rufibarbis*, by Steve Gschmeissner

ISBN 0 9526065 9 3

British Library Cataloguing-in-Publication Data.
A catalogue record for this book is available
from the British Library.

First published 2005
by Surrey Wildlife Trust
School Lane, Pirbright, Woking, Surrey GU24 0JN.

Produced by Wellset Repro Ltd, Cranleigh.

FOREWORD

It gives me great pleasure to introduce John Pontin's excellent account of Surrey Ants. This has real relevance to me. My family acquired a simple cottage set in a sort of mini-wilderness of several acres about a mile south of Camberley. It was wonderful during my teenage years, having had a lively interest in ants since I was eight, to become closely acquainted with Wood Ants, Slavemakers, glossy Jet Black Ants and many other species in a varied habitat of *Molinia* bog, birch scrub and adjacent pinewoods.

The M3 motorway extinguished the *Molinia* bog, while the rest of the property was sold and for the past thirty years has been an expensive residential suburb. It is of great importance to retain as much as possible of Surrey's heathland, natural woodland and plantations as refuges for wildlife.

John Pontin has made a fine contribution to Surrey's Wildlife Atlas series based on his many original research papers and a lifetime of keen observations on the behaviour of ants and their ecological relationships with aphids, competing ant species and other arthropods.

CEDRIC COLLINGWOOD

To Ros

CONTENTS

A N T S unite together in Colonies, which they form in such Places and Situations as are most agreeable to their different Natures, and the Management of their Affairs.

From *Gould on Ants*, by the Rev William Gould, published in 1747.

INTRODUCTORY BIOLOGY

Ants are among the most interesting animals on earth even though they are not large or beautiful. The main interest is usually in their societies, which may be analagous to human societies, but this is misleading because no thinking is used to maintain them. They can learn from experience, but innate response to stimuli is the main organising method. Ants also have great abundance which results in many interactions with other species and high ecological impact, that will be observed by anyone making records in the field for an atlas, so these features are reviewed briefly in the following paragraphs.

Ants belong to the insect order Hymenoptera and are included with the bees and wasps in the subgroup Aculeata. This latter name means that stings have been evolved from modified ovipositors, but two of the main groups of ants have lost this weapon and very few of the others in Britain can sting us effectively.

All ants are social with a perennial colony organisation similar to that of hive-bees. Each nest has at least one specialist egg-laying queen and many wingless, non-reproducing, female workers. The different forms of individuals in one nest are termed castes.

The communication needed to integrate nestmates into a co-operating group is mainly chemical, but also with tactile stimulation using the antennae. Each nest has a distinctive odour which is primarily inherited, but can be partly acquired, and foreigners of the same or different species are quickly recognised. As a result, each nest of ants maintains an exclusive territory by direct attack using the jaws or stings, or by chemical repellents.

The ants feed each other, mouth to mouth, by regurgitation of liquid from a crop – a process termed trophallaxis.

Winged males and queens (alates) are reared each year in a specific season which is typically in summer although there are exceptions. They make spectacular massed mating flights, in the case of a number of abundant species. The males die after mating or after a short adult life of a few weeks. The winged queens select suitable sites to start new nests and cast off their wings on alighting. There is a weak zone very close to the body, and the wings snap off on being bent down by the legs.

The eggs are small and hatch after a few days, depending on temperature, into legless larvae which are fed by regurgitation. The queen takes off for her mating flight with a crop full of food, and this is supplemented by internal breakdown of the wing muscles that are no longer needed. The larva and pupa stages of *Lasius* may each take a few weeks at summer temperatures, and the large queens of *Formica, Lasius* and *Tetramorium* can produce a few abnormally small workers in their first September, after mating in July.

They do not need to forage for food during this time, but the smaller queens of other genera may need to do so.

The nests do not have eggs or pupae in winter, and those of *Formica* do not have any immatures at all during the winter. The normal number of workers in one nest varies widely with the species and can, for example, build up to 30,000 in the common garden *Lasius* or much more in the Wood Ant. The alates of the next generation are only produced when appropriately large numbers of workers are present.

Queens in mature nests develop large ovaries which swell their bodies to an obvious extent, a condition called physogastric. Egg-laying takes place in the spring and especially once the over-wintering larvae pupate and the food intake is switched to the queen. Fast egg production is needed to replace the enormous numbers of workers which can live for several years to maintain the perennial nests, but which frequently die much younger in defence of the nest or in tackling fierce prey. *Lasius* queens can lay 100 eggs in an hour!

All British species eat small invertebrates which they find dead or they kill by biting and stinging or squirting chemicals onto them. Only the Wood Ant and its close relatives produce large quantities of formic acid. Most ants of other genera use quite different chemicals which, in the case of *Lasius* and *Tapinoma*, are easily smelt by us. Some items of prey are much larger than the ants but they can be killed by a mass attack, even sacrificing some workers if there is a net gain for the society. The blood of the insect prey is swallowed by the foragers, but solid food is carried back to the nest and given to the larvae. Turning over a stone covering a nest may reveal larvae with items of food on them, and this enables an observer to assess the range of food taken.

Most species also use another major source of food. Plant-sucking insects take in far more carbohydrates than they can use themselves, and this is voided as sweet faeces called "honeydew". Aphids and coccids are commonly attended by ants which stroke them with their antennae and wait for droplets of honeydew to appear. The honeydew may be retained until an ant gives this stimulation, so the association has clearly evolved into a very close and interesting one. It can also be very complicated and will be dealt with at greater length in the section on myrmecophily. This term includes a wide variety of non-antagonistic relationships between ants and other organisms.

Ants can navigate home by using the sun as a compass, through an internal time sense to allow for its relative movement across the sky. They can also learn landmarks, including the pattern of the tree canopy in open woodland.

The efficiency of foraging is often improved by laying scent trails to persistent food sources such as colonies of aphids. The returning ants, full of liquid food, mark the surface they walk on with spots of scent which persist long enough for outgoing ants to follow the trail and reinforce it if successful.

Extra-floral nectaries, such as those near the top of very young bracken fronds, are used by ants as a carbohydrate source, but flowers may also be visited.

ECOLOGICAL IMPACT BY ANTS

Invertebrates need their own protection from predatory ants, or they need to evolve "friendly" associations with ants that are known as "myrmecophily".

Running, jumping, flying, repugnant chemicals, long dense hair, mucus covering, silk shelters, heavy smooth armour, very small size and living inside plant tissues can all have some protective value. Returning the ants' aggression is not usually a valuable reaction, because ants can readily attract a mass of attacking recruits and, since workers are sterile, they may be sacrificed to gain a larger item of prey.

The impact of ants is often made worse because their populations of territories can saturate a habitat leaving nowhere for unprotected species to avoid ant attack. For example *Lasius flavus* is easily observed to reach a high density of nests in old pasture, each mound being about two metres from its nearest neighbour. Other habitats are less uniformly suitable, so nests of other ants are usually less conspicuous, but those of the Wood Ant can also be very densely distributed. In this case, however, one society of ants can occupy several nests ("polydomous") and the spacing of mounds is less regular.

Ants can be their own worst enemies and the ecological impact on other ant species is extreme. Predation is not unusual, but coexistence of different species can be maintained in several ways. The ants need to avoid or survive an attack, both when foraging and when defending their nests.

Small ants have special problems if they live within the foraging range of larger ones. *Tapinoma* uses a chemical repellent, in the same manner as a skunk, and can even repel the large and aggressive *F.sanguinea*. *Leptothorax* is the complete opposite, since it avoids attack by not being detected. This presumably means that it does not provide chemical cues to other ants and is the equivalent of being invisible in a visual world. This has the disadvantage that scent trails cannot be used to communicate the location of a food source to nestmates. "Pair-running" behaviour is used instead, in which the first ant to return from food leads another one back to it, keeping close contact. On their return, each ant then recruits another, and by further repetition this method is surprisingly effective in building up a large number of foragers.

Other methods of species avoidance include the use of a different "habitat layer". For example, *L.flavus* is subterranean and coexists with *L.niger* which has much larger territories above ground. They also have different repellent chemicals which help maintain the separation. *L.fuliginosus* and *F.rufa* both forage on trees and canalise their foraging along scent trails from their nests to each tree. Gaps are left between these trails on the ground, so *M.ruginodis* can nest and forage there at lower levels. It is, however, not immune from having its nests raided and brood eaten by either of the trail makers. Where abundant enough, *L.fuliginosus* and *F.rufa* defend mutually exclusive territories against each other. This pattern is commoner in species-rich habitats abroad, where it is termed a "mosaic".

IMPACT ON PLANTS

Only one British ant species, *Tetramorium caespitum*, eats seeds – they are fed to its larvae, or stored when abundant. However some plants, such as violets, produce seeds with a special stalk (caruncle) which is attractive to ants. Any ant foraging above ground will pick up these seeds and carry them back to its nest, without damaging them enough to stop germination. The seeds of violets have been the subject of research which has found that transport by ants is important for dispersal. The ants carry the seeds to sunnier sites, bite off the caruncles and then dump the hard smooth seeds in a midden outside the nest, along with nitrogen-rich insect debris.

MYRMECOPHILY

This term includes a remarkable range of symbiotic and parasitic organisms evolved to live with ants. A number of them are certain to be found by anyone studying ants, so a brief review of some examples is worth including in an atlas. Donisthorpe's *Guests of British Ants* (1927) is the last book to attempt general coverage of the subject and is still interesting, but much further research has been done on some of the examples.

The most famous case is that of the Large Blue Butterfly, *Maculinea arion*, whose small larvae are carried by workers of *Myrmica sabuleti* into their nest. Like many other Lycaenid butterfly larvae, they use secretions that attract ants and so inhibit the ants from eating them. The larvae of the Large Blue feed on ant larvae, grow to full size and pupate in the nest. Although the ant is common in Surrey, the butterfly has never been recorded here. It became extinct from all known British sites because of loss of hot habitat for the ant, but has been successfully re-introduced. The other Lycaenids in Britain have not been investigated so thoroughly. Pupae of the Silver-studded Blue (*Plebejus argus*) are found in nests of *Lasius niger, L.platythorax* and probably other "black" *Lasius*. In captivity the adults lay eggs more freely in the presence of ants, especially the very smelly *L.fuliginosus* which is probably not a natural host. Larvae of the Chalkhill Blue (*Lysandra coridon*) and Adonis Blue (*L.bellargus*) live on chalk downland and are usually attended by *Myrmica* or *Lasius*. These larvae can be reared on their food-plants and so are probably not predaceous on ant brood, but gain some protection from predators by their association with ants.

Myrmecophiles that eat their hosts tend to be very specific to one host, which is presumably because they must match the host's chemical recognition signals closely, or the host will evolve defences against them. Species with this behaviour are found in other insect orders, for example the Staphylinid beetle *Lomechusa strumosa* which lives in nests of the Slavemaker, *F.sanguinea*, and, in captivity, eats the ant's larvae. The beetle larvae are treated as ant larvae by the host and look superficially rather like them, but they do have short legs. The adult also is myrmecophilous in this case, unlike the previous examples.

Another beetle with interesting behaviour is *Amphotis marginata*. It is usually found on the scent trails of *L.fuliginosus* where it begs food from returning ants as though it were itself an ant. Ants full of honeydew feed it by regurgitation, but empty ants will attack it if they notice it at all. Its shape, rather like a soldier's steel helmet with reflexed edges, helps it to resist attack by tucking in all its appendages and lowering itself closely onto the surface.

The hoverfly *Microdon analis* is widespread on the Surrey heaths and is another example of a predatory larva with a free-flying adult. It is worth including because it illustrates the importance of naming the host species and retaining specimens of it. It was recorded to live with *L.niger*, but now that it has been realised that "*L.niger*" is actually two species, the correct host cannot be identified unless specimens of it have been kept. The larvae of *Microdon* are legless and slug-like, so the dead wood of nests of *L.platythorax* is a more suitable substrate than the loose soil particles of nests of *L.niger*, and, indeed, the modern records are from nests of *L.platythorax*.

Many myrmecophiles with little smell of their own acquire the odour of the nest and live unnoticed by the ants. A very common example, which can live with almost any species of ant, is a small white woodlouse called *Platyarthrus hoffmannseggi*. It is most abundant in the rubbish-dump areas of nests and may be just a scavenger, but little information is recorded about its biology.

The excretions of plant-sucking bugs can be an essential food resource for ants, and this mutually beneficial relationship has obviously evolved closely into a very complex one. However, it is highly interesting to biologists and is easily observed, so a summary of the interaction of ants and aphids is included here.

There are many myrmecophilous species of aphids and they differ in anatomy and in behaviour from non-myrmecophilous ones. For example, the non-myrmecophilous greenfly of roses (*Macrosiphum rosae*) has long legs and well-developed sense organs (long antennae and large eyes), and produces numerous winged individuals. Most importantly, it has a finger-like projection to flick liquid faeces away and two long tubes projecting rearward from its back. These tubes are called cornicles and can squirt a sticky liquid, which hardens in the air, onto its enemies, and the aphid may then walk away to escape. Ants are treated as enemies, so many aphid species with this behaviour are eaten as prey by ants. On the other hand, myrmecophilous aphids typically have shorter legs and antennae, smaller eyes, and the cornicles either very short or completely absent. They retain drops of faeces on a ring of hairs around the anus. Ants feed on the sugary faeces, which are produced in response to contact from the ants' antennae, and can be withdrawn inside if not taken.

The aphids may benefit from the association with ants through gaining protection from attack by parasites and predators, for which the main evidence is the loss of the aphids' defence organs. Removal of honeydew, which might otherwise foul the aphid habitat, could also be a factor.

This extraordinary degree of specialising evolution can be taken further. For example, *L.flavus* has acquired a range of underground aphid species which, in Britain, have lost their sexual generations on woody plants and are continuously asexual on the roots or stolons of grasses. They may, however, have sexual generations abroad, on the non-British *Pistacia* (aphid genera *Forda, Geoica and Baizongia*), on elm where available (*Tetraneura*) or on *Cornus* (*Anoecia*) (occasionally in Britain). Others may lay over-wintering eggs (e.g. *Sappaphis bonomii* on Wild Parsnip) which are tended by the ants as though they were out-of-season ant eggs. *L.flavus* feeds large numbers of these root aphids to its larvae and is assumed to use its aphid cultures for prey as well as sources of honeydew. Winged myrmecophilous aphids are comparatively rare because dispersal is less important and it is risky to leave the ants' protection. Also, the usual reason for production of alate aphids, overcrowding, does not normally occur when with *L.flavus*.

The *Lasius* species which forage above ground are less closely adapted to their aphids, but *L.fuliginosus* sometimes guards the eggs of *Stomaphis*, a very large aphid dwelling on tree trunks.

Most myrmecophilous aphids can be associated with a wide range of ant species because they are recognised as food sources. However, *Tetramorium* has a specific subterranean aphid, *Paracletus cimiciformis*, which is usually found loose in the ants' tunnels. Its host plant was a mystery, but in captivity it can be fed on grass stolons. Under these conditions it is attacked by *Lasius* species, so records with *L.flavus* are likely to be misidentifications of the aphid.

The aphid group *Tramini* are also subterranean and have elongated hind-legs which are not used for walking, but are used to communicate with ants as though they were antennae. Honeydew is passed to the ant in the same manner as an ant passing regurgitated food to another one. The large aphids on conifers (*Cinara*) and similar black species on roses (*Maculolachnus*) and on oak (*Lachnus*) may also perform this type of feeding through communication.

The common garden blackfly (*Aphis* spp.) may be tended by ants, but are often without ants. Their anatomy is intermediate between the extreme myrmecophiles and the greenfly. They do, however, retain honeydew droplets for ants when present.

It has been suggested that some ants can use honeydew as their only food source. This is not as far-fetched as it might seem, because, although honeydew is mainly sugar and water, some amino-acids (protein building-blocks) are passed out by aphids and these might be altered (transaminated) into the appropriate protein components needed by ants. The ants do have internal micro-organisms which could do this and it would be an extra incentive for the ants to defend aphids.

One further topic should also be reviewed before leaving this brief summary of myrmecophily. Protection of aphids by ants is definitely not complete, because a few members of each group of insects which attack aphids have in their turn become myrmecophilous!

A good example is *Coccinella magnifica*, a ladybird resembling the common Seven-spot (*C.septempunctata*), which is associated with the Wood Ant (*F.rufa*) or sometimes the Slavemaker (*F.sanguinea*). *C.magnifica* feeds on tended aphids without any reaction by the ants, but *C.septempunctata*, like other non-myrmecophilous insects, is attacked. *Platynaspis luteorubra* is a small ladybird which has woodlouse-shaped larvae, a shape common in myrmecophiles. These larvae can attack subterranean aphids accompanied by *Lasius*. Similarly, some hoverfly larvae (e.g. *Pipizella*) and an internal hymenopterous parasite, *Paralipsis*, also attack subterranean aphids, especially those living superficially on the root-collars of plants. *Paralipsis* goes even further since, when adult, it is fed by workers of *L.niger* as though it were an ant.

HABITATS AND CONSERVATION

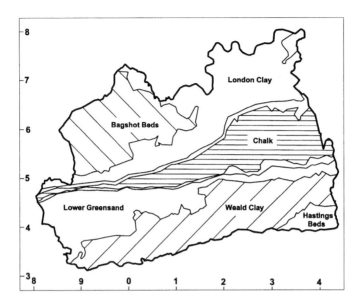

In common with many invertebrates in Britain, the ambient temperature is seldom high enough for the growth and development of ants. Of the thirty Surrey species, seventeen need habitats in full sun, only eight can survive in fully shaded nest sites, and only four of these reach full success without some sun. The woodland species with large nests, for example *Lasius fuliginosus* and *Formica rufa*, live in nests that insulate the brood from external conditions and retain the metabolic heat generated by ant activity. *F.rufa* needs sun in the spring and basks in masses on the surface of the nest, although it can be fully shaded later on, when the trees are in leaf.

The habitats with a high priority are heathland in its pioneer stage with bare patches, and grazed south-facing chalk scarps with stable stones on the surface. Mature heather can be so dense that it is effectively woodland for many soil-inhabiting insects, including ants.

Planting of trees (often by well-meaning managers) is a particularly damaging treatment of previously open sites, and dense conifer plantations are usually without ants, except at the edge.

Drainage is also important. Only the rare *F.picea* normally inhabits quaking bogs, although the common species may be found in large tussocks. Far too many heaths in Surrey are too wet in winter for the dry heath species (*Tetramorium, Tapinoma, F.rufibarbis* and *Lasius psammophilus*) while too dry in summer for *F.picea* and *Myrmica sulcinodis*. Ridges and humps, instead of level ground, can overcome this problem if they are tall enough and extensive enough. If the dead stumps of trees cleared by managers are left to decay, then *L.platythorax*, *F.fusca* and *Leptothorax acervorum* may become abundant, but these are more generally distributed in any case.

Myrmecina and *Ponera* appear to be rather special in needing hot places which are never severely dry. They also avoid waterlogging by occupying banks, and are most frequently found in clay patches on chalk scarps with short plant cover. The average temperature, a few degrees higher, is presumably the reason why they are being recorded in south London.

The problem is, as usual: how do we maintain suitable conditions to conserve the desired species? Ants are peculiar in being perennial insects needing several years for nests to mature and ten or more years to achieve total reproductive potential. The difficulty is made worse because many species also need vegetation at a pioneer stage for successful colonisation of an area as well as for the prolonged survival of nests.

A second peculiarity of ant populations, in general, is that the true population number can be very small even though there are, misleadingly, thousands of ants present. For example, in the case of the endangered *F.rufibarbis*, there may be only one reproducing individual (queen) in each 100 square metres of territory! Large areas of habitat are therefore particularly valuable.

HEATHLANDS

With 60 years experience of studying natural history on the dry heaths of southern England, it has become clear that plant succession has become much faster. There are two obvious causes of this: the increased nitrogen deposition from vehicle exhausts, and also fouling by animals which have been fed away from the heath. Neither of these factors is easy to prevent, and management is desperately needed to conserve sparse and short vegetation for soil-living insects.

The ants of dry heath have become rarer, the most extreme example being *F.rufibarbis* which is reduced to two sites in mainland Britain with a total of only four known nests. *Tapinoma* is similarly reduced in Surrey, with no recent records from many heaths, including Chobham Common where it was recorded 40 years ago, while *Tetramorium* is numerous on the larger dry heaths but severely reduced on Chobham Common. This latter species is the host of the very rare workerless ant *Anergates*, which, in Surrey, has only been recorded twice, most recently from Ash ranges.

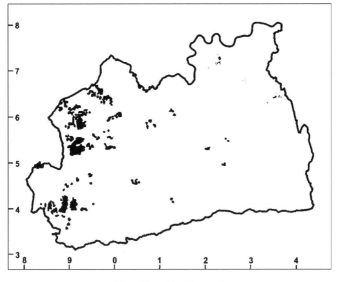

Heathland in Surrey [1]

Tapinoma is vulnerable to fires and trampling because of its superficial nests, but the other species of dry heaths, including also *L.psammophilus* and *L.meridionalis*, survive fires easily. Summer fires in dry conditions produce an ideal bare surface without any insulating peat or debris, but the control of fires and cooperation with conservers of other organisms are both difficult problems that have prevented fires from being used often enough. The most extensive and ant-rich heathlands in Surrey are those in the large area from Ash Ranges to Lightwater Heath, where the only "management" happening for most of the twentieth century was summer burning. They would not be there, but for this, and together they form one of the outstanding heath areas of England.

Tracks can be useful for providing bare edges for nest sites, but the amount of trampling is critical. Human feet usually do not cause too much disturbance of the edges, but horse tracks can easily become covered by unsuitable loose sand.

[1] Sources for map:
   a) Hicks, M.J., 1986. *A field survey of Surrey heathland 1985*. Nature Conservancy Council internal report.
   b) London Biodiversity Partnership.

GRASSLAND

Grazing has the disadvantage, for soil-inhabiting insects, of trampling damage. However, sheep-grazed chalk downland may retain *Ponera, Myrmecina, L.alienus, F.cunicularia* and *Myrmica sabuleti* in good numbers, because embedded surface stones are preserved and not shaded by the short turf. Monitoring sites on the North Downs has recorded reduced numbers of these species following the removal of sheep. Unfortunately, the ant populations have not recovered, even though ponies and goats have replaced the sheep. The main fault is disturbance of the surface stones by heavy-footed grazers on the steep slopes.

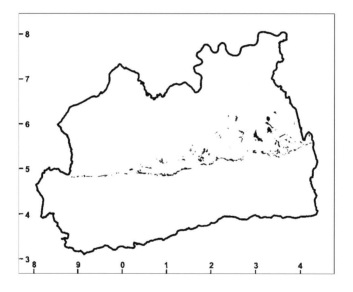

Chalk grassland in Surrey [2]

My research plots at Englefield Green, on acid sandy grassland, were managed by Soay sheep which were ideal for retaining *L.niger*. The coexisting *L.flavus* is exceptional in withstanding heavy grazing by cattle and horses (for example on Staines Moor).

[2] Sources for map:
  a) Humphreys, S.J., 2000. *A survey to identify chalk grassland in Surrey using aerial photographs in combination with information from previous field surveys.* University of Surrey, unpublished MSc dissertation report.
  b) London Biodiversity Partnership.

WOODLAND

F.rufa, L.brunneus, L.fuliginosus, L.umbratus, Leptothorax nylanderi, Stenamma and *Formicoxenus nitidulus* form a suite of species which can coexist without mutual interference, except that the two large tree foragers, *L.fuliginosus* and *F.rufa*, occupy separate territories without any overlap in foraging area. The others differ from each other in their mode of life, or have special coexistence strategies which are described under "Ecological Impact by Ants" (page 11) or under their specific headings. *Myrmica ruginodis* is also common in woodland and occupies any gaps in the surface foraging area of the others, but it does this in other habitats as well.

Only Wentworth Great Wood has all these species, but their habitat has now been reduced in area through a change of management.

OTHER LAND USE

Intensive agriculture and management for sports result in an absence of ants, mainly because of annual cultivation, heavy grazing or the use of insecticides. Even so-called "organic" agriculture could possibly be counterproductive for conservation if it means that a larger area of cultivation is needed to produce the same amount of human food.

Sunningdale golf course is an interesting compromise where heathland has been retained between the fairways. All the heath ant species are still there, except *Tapinoma*, which was there before1970, and *F.rufibarbis* which has never been recorded there.

The national status of rare species is assessed for conservation purposes in Falk's review listed in the bibliography.

FIELD ASSESSMENT OF DISTRIBUTION AND ABUNDANCE

In order to test the effects of management, or other changes in the environment, or nest changes from year to year, it will be necessary to use experimental methods, which also sometimes reveal species which are difficult to find by normal methods of collecting.

One approach is to place a line of artificial nest sites in sunny areas, spaced out across the habitat zones. This is usually called a transect, and the attractive artificial hotspots may be tiles or crushed cans, which become hot in the sun. Baits of minced meat can be added as a further attraction. Pitfall trapping can also be used if samples of dead ants are required. These methods can distort the behaviour of the ants or introduce a bias in favour of the most active species, but it is easy to demonstrate the survival of nests after a fire, or their loss by trampling. *Myrmecina* and *Ponera* are found on chalk grassland much more readily than by any ordinary collecting method.

Estimating the number of ants in a nest is difficult because of the large numbers involved, so this has not been done for most of our species. An estimate can be obtained by marking a counted sample, returning it to the nest and, after allowing time for mixing, counting another sample to find the ratio of marked to unmarked individuals. Nests of *L.flavus* have been estimated, using radioactive tracer marking, to reach at least twenty thousand workers in large nests and this can laboriously be confirmed by sharing out a dug-up nest among a class of students for manual counting! Much larger numbers are clearly present in some nests of the Wood Ant, and possibly those of other species too.

A very rough comparison of worker numbers in different nests of a species which feeds above ground can be made by observing the numbers attracted to a feeding dish of sugar solution. This has been useful to assess the viability of the nests of *F.rufibarbis* without needing to interfere seriously with them.

The use of a Tullgren funnel, by applying heat to extract specimens from samples of soil or leaf litter, enables densities to be measured for ecological studies. This can be especially valuable for studying subterranean species, for example *L.flavus*.

NAMES AND NAMING

English names have been invented for many British ant species, but most of them have not been generally accepted. They can also be very confusing when very similar species are newly recognised and added to the faunal list. The formal latinised names are more stable and are used here, along with a few well-established English names.

Unfortunately there are very few currently available books which have up-to-date nomenclature, but *The Ants (Hymenoptera, Formicidae) of Poland* by Czechowski, Radchenko and Czechowska (published in Warsaw, 2002, ISBN 83-85192-98) is a valuable source, in English, of identification keys for British and European species. Their nomenclature will be used here. Additional keys and useful drawings will be found in Collingwood's *The Formicidae (Hymenoptera) of Fennoscandia and Denmark* and the bibliography will refer you to a key published by Sweeney and also *Naturalist's Handbooks, No. 24: Ants*, by Skinner and Allen (published by Richmond), which is more readily available.

Other literature may use different names and this can be the result of synonyms which have been rejected by Czechowski *et al.*, or the over-zealous splitting of genera. The traditional generic limits will be retained here, in order to keep names stable and the genera usefully large.

The following simplified key is an introductory one and is limited to the worker caste of species found in Surrey.

THE STRUCTURE OF ANTS

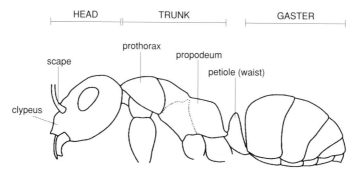

Formicinae
(e.g. *Formica fusca*)

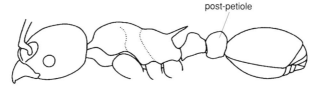

Myrmicinae
(e.g. *Myrmica schencki*)

Dolichoderinae
(e.g. *Tapinoma erraticum*)

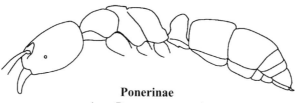

Ponerinae
(e.g. *Ponera coarctata*)

AN INTRODUCTORY KEY TO <u>WORKERS</u> OF THE ANTS RECORDED IN SURREY

This key is intended only for beginners, and leaves several difficult problems unsolved, but most of these concern species which beginners are unlikely to find at first.

Queens, which are not dealt with, are distinguished by possessing a large thorax to house the wing muscles. Males, with two exceptions, have wings.

A general naturalist will find that familiarity with the three main genera, *Lasius, Formica* and *Myrmica*, is valuable as a first stage. Distinction of the species does, however, become important for ecology and when studying the other insects associated with ants.

Reference specimens of closely related species are valuable, and sometimes essential, when using this key.

Experience of teaching introductory ant courses has shown that line drawings are often insufficient for naming species, because they are difficult to relate to specimens. Therefore some macrophotographs are included in the colour plates, in the hope that they will help with the identification of some difficult species. Scanning electron micrographs also tend to be unrealistic, but are valuable to show detail surface sculpture and pilosity. Some of *Myrmica* species have been published by Wardlaw, Elmes and Thomas.

1

(See figures opposite and colour plates 14-16.)

Waist of ant with two similar-sized segments. Sting present. (Pupae naked.)............
....**Myrmicinae 2**

Waist with only one segment forming a vertical scale. Posterior orifice circular, surrounded by fringe of hairs. Sting absent. (Pupae usually in cocoons.)..................
....**Formicinae 12**

Waist segment hidden from above under the front of the gaster. Posterior orifice a transverse slit. Sting absent. (Pupae naked. Small black heathland species.)............
.... **Dolichoderinae, *Tapinoma erraticum* (page 72)**

Waist a thick segment followed by an abdominal segment slightly constricted behind to form a second waist much thicker than the first. Sting present. Very small and slim. (Pupae in cocoons) .... **Ponerinae, *Ponera coarctata* (page 73)**

Myrmicinae

2

Post-petiole with ventral spine. (Only found as an inquiline in Wood Ant nests. Males worker-like with longer curved antennae.)..
...........................*Formicoxenus nitidulus* **(page 67)**

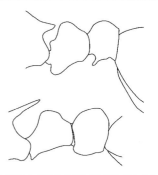

Post-petiole without spine......................................3

3

Antennae 11-segmented with darkened clubs. Resembles a small slim *Myrmica*. (Typically nesting in dead wood.)......................*Leptothorax acervorum* **(page 65)**

Antennae 12-segmented with clubs similar in colour to the rest of the antenna **4**

4

Clypeus with two anterior teeth. (Small, blackish, slow-moving and may stay still and rolled-up when disturbed.). ....*Myrmecina graminicola* **(page 69)**

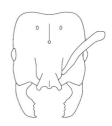

Clypeus without teeth **5**

5

Prothorax with angled corners as seen from above. (Small, blackish, active, aggressive and stinging.) ....
.... *Tetramorium caespitum* **(page 70)**

(Alate females and pupoid males with *Tetramorium*, and which are a similar size to *Tetramorium* workers, are the workerless parasite *Anergates atratulus*.)

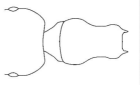

Prothorax with a rounded anterior **6**

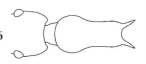

6

Petiole elongate and twice as long as tall. Slow-moving, small and slender with reduced eyes ....
.... *Stenamma* **(page 68)**

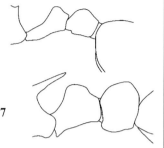

Petiole not clearly longer than tall and eyes with normal multi-facets 7

7

Terminal segments of the antennae forming a 3-segmented club which is shorter than the rest of the funiculus. Body length normally > 4mm **8**

Antennal club of similar length to the rest of the funiculus. Body length < 3.5mm. (Typically nesting in the bark of trees.) ....*Leptothorax nylanderi* **(page 66)**

Myrmica

8

Antennal scape curved towards the base, but not sharply angled..**9**

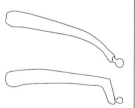

Scape with a sharp angle near the base so that the ball-and-socket articulation with the head is displaced out of line with the shaft of the scape.......................................**11**

9

Propodeal spines as long as the distance between their tips and with striations between their bases **10**

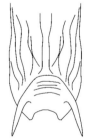

Propodeal spines shorter than the distance between their tips and with a smooth area between their bases..........*M.rubra* **(page 58)**

10

Spines divergent. Trunk brown and a similar shade to the head and gaster in mature specimens. Scape gently curved at the base. (Abundant, shade-tolerant and widespread.)...*M.ruginodis* (page 59)

Spines nearly parallel with convergent tips. Trunk paler than head and with a black gaster. (Nests in peaty humps on wet heaths.) ....*M.sulcinodis* (page 60)

11

Scape with a scale-like flange around the shaft close to the base..............................
....*M.schencki* (page 63)

Scape with a tooth at the base. Typically with a blackish gaster ....
....*M.lobicornis* (page 63)

Scape with a keel running along the shaft near the base...........*M.sabuleti* (page 62)

Scape without these features. Petiole with a truncate flat top.....................................
....*M.scabrinodis* (page 61)

Formicinae

12

Propodeal spiracle round in side view and close to the posterior surface of the propodeum. Segments 2-5 of the funiculus shorter than the others. (Male much smaller than a queen; larvae present in winter.) ....*Lasius* **13**

Propodeal spiracle slit-like or narrowly elliptical, and distant from the posterior surface of the propodeum. Segments 2-5 of the funiculus not shorter than the others. (Larger, faster-running and usually very aware of the observer; male and queen of similar size; no brood in winter.).. *Formica* **19**

Lasius

13

Shining black with an emarginate back of the head. (Diagnostic smell; follows scent trails; carton nest in rotting wood.)....**Jet Black Ant,** *L.fuliginosus* **(page 50)**

Uniformly dull blackish or dark brown **14**

Yellow (sometimes brownish in large individuals.)..**16**

Head and trunk brown, gaster dark grey or black. (Nest in bark or dead wood of standing trees; non-aggressive.)................ **Brown Tree Ant,** *L.brunneus* **(page 44)**

14

Scapes and tibiae with many obvious erect hairs...
.... **Garden Black Ant,** *L.niger* **(page 39)** or *L.platythorax* **(page 41)**

(The differences between their workers are small and need microscope work, but the queens are clearly distinct. *L.platythorax* has queens with a much shallower thorax relative to its width. It is also more shade-tolerant and more frequently nests in dead wood.)

Scapes and tibiae without erect hairs **15**

15

Two to five hairs on rear of propodeum below the spiracle on each side. Appears paler brown than *L.alienus* when alive. (Nesting on dry sandy heaths under bare surfaces in the sun.)...................................
.... ***L.psammophilus*** **(page 43)**

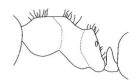

Propodeum bare at the rear except for an occasional single hair. Blacker than L.psammophilus when alive. (Nesting in hot sites on chalk downland.)...................
.... ***L.alienus*** **(page 42)**

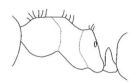

16

Erect hairs on tibiae and scapes **17**

No erect hairs on tibiae and scapes..**18**

17

Scapes round in cross-section at mid-length. (Carton nests in rotten wood, typically in woodland shade.) ....***L.umbratus*** **(page 47)**

Scapes flattened with a ridge along the leading edge, most easily seen in queens but can be difficult to see in workers. (Carton nests, most frequent on heathland, but sometimes in shade.)...***L.meridionalis*** **(page 48)**

18

Body hairs short – those on top of the gaster less than a third of tibia width. (Nests subterranean in dead wood.) .... ***L.mixtus*** **(page 49)**

Body hairs much longer. (Characteristically making mound nests with plant cover in pasture.)..**Yellow Meadow Ant,** ***L.flavus*** **(page 45)**

Formica

19

Anterior of clypeus with a central emargination or notch. Legs and trunk red, with red or brownish head and dark grey or black gaster. Smaller individuals darker. (Usually with black workers of *F.fusca* in the same nest. Usually on heathland in dead wood or in sunny banks.) ....**Slavemaker, *F.sanguinea* (page 53)**

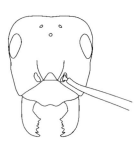

Clypeus without any indentation in the anterior margin...**20**

20

Uniformly black with a few standing hairs on top of the prothorax. (Nest normally in or near quaking bogs.) .... **Black Bog Ant, *F.picea* (page 57)**

Black with a bare thorax and a silky sheen on the gaster. (Common species in pioneer dry habitats.)..*F.fusca* (page 54)**

Black or dark grey with reddish sides to the head and often with red areas on the trunk **21**

21

Frontal triangle shiny. (Typically with a large mound of vegetable debris as a nest.) .... **Wood Ant, *F.rufa* (page 51)**

Frontal triangle dull matt **22**

22

Forward-leaning hairs on top of the prothorax. Legs darker than trunk. (Aggressive when nest approached. Endangered species, in hottest spots on heathland.) ....*F.rufibarbis* (page 55)**

Prothorax bare or occasionally with one or two hairs. Legs red in individuals with a red trunk, but this difference most obvious when alive. (Hot sites on chalk or heath.)..*F.cunicularia* (page 55)**

MAKING A COLLECTION FOR IDENTIFICATION OF SPECIES

The removal of a few workers or alate sexuals from a well-established nest has a negligible effect on the remaining colony. Collecting these is therefore harmless, and it is very important to make a collection for the identification and recording of all species of ants. Furthermore, it is often valuable to keep several specimens, including all the castes, for identification of even some of the commonest species. This will become clear when using the species accounts and the identification key. It is also possible that, in future, further species will be recognised which are at present confused with and included in a familiar species, because of their extreme similarity of appearance. These are termed "sibling species" and they are often seen to have biological differences once the anatomical differences have been recognised. Earlier records will be of dubious value unless suitable specimens have been retained.

Functional queens should not be collected (especially of rare species) but, after a mating flight, the freshly mated queens have only a very small chance of successfully starting a colony and they may be used for a collection or kept alive to rear captive observation nests.

COLLECTING AND OBSERVING METHODS

A X10 hand lens is useful for identification in the field, but higher magnification under a binocular microscope may be needed to confirm the more difficult cases.

A pooter (a device for sucking small insects into specimen tubes) is very useful for picking up small ants, but their chemical secretions may be too objectionable for continual use. Aspirators powered by an electric fan may be better, but commercially available ones can be too feeble for many species. Alternatively, active charcoal filters are a possible precaution when regularly using lung power, but here again, suction may be made too feeble. Many Formicines are killed by their own chemicals in bare specimen tubes, but the inclusion of dusty soil can prevent this when specimens are needed alive. Young queens are similarly vulnerable, so it is preferable to sweep them into a tube with a small watercolour brush if they are to be kept alive.

Most species will be found by making a visual search for foragers, turning over stones, or disturbing the surface of likely nest sites with a trowel or knife. Sweep-netting and beating of foliage are also valuable methods for collecting those species foraging on the upper parts of plants. Alates are often caught in Malaise traps and light traps.

Ants may be killed by deep-freezing, either for examination or for making a permanent collection.

It is not usual to mount ants for a collection by piercing them with pins. Some of them are too small for this, and many species may be examined more easily through a microscope if they are mounted on the point of a narrow triangular piece of card. Individuals from the same nest should be on points mounted on the same pin or, if many spare specimens are available, they may be kept in a gelatine capsule on the same pin. It may be necessary to examine specimens from various angles under a microscope, so specimens mounted in a variety of positions would then be helpful. If only one is available, some thought should be given to the arrangement of its posture for viewing the critical features.

It should go without saying that labels, recording at least the locality, date of capture and name of collector, are impaled on the same pin. If possible, the habitat, nest type and/or behaviour should be added.

Dead ants eventually fade, so the colour of very old specimens cannot be relied on for identification. Also, newly hatched individuals are usually paler than mature ones, while very old specimens may have lost their pilosity by abrasion and so may be more difficult to name.

ENCLOSURES FOR OBSERVATION AND REARING IN CAPTIVITY

When pupae have been found, the sexual castes may be reared in captivity, but this requires suitable conditions for the survival of a group of workers to nurse them. The behaviour of ants is captivating, but the reader is warned that keeping artificial nests becomes an addictive hobby!

In *British Ants*, Donisthorpe describes the traditional methods which will work for a short-term study, but they are unnecessarily complicated and not at all practical for any study taking more than a year. Plaster of Paris nests are frequently suggested, but this becomes very messy since it dissolves slowly in water. Other mouldable materials are not sufficiently porous for direct substitution, and a damp area in each nest is needed.

A much simpler arrangement works better than any of the more complex ones. All that is needed is a transparent polystyrene box with a rod of firebrick cemented into a hole in the bottom and dipping into a vessel of water beneath. Firebrick is porous enough to provide a local wet surface while being too hard for any of our species to bite through. The result can be seen in the photograph of *Myrmecina* – a species which chooses to live on a damp patch.

No soil is used, since it soaks up water and removes the choice of wet or dry substrate, while the ants can use it to obscure the view. A ventilation window can be useful, if covered with metal gauze. If the nest is to be kept for several years, then de-ionised water should be used to avoid lime-scale problems. Eventually, clean nests may need to be provided. The ants will transfer themselves if a fresh nest is connected to the old one by a glass tube inserted into accurately drilled holes in each of them. Darkness is not essential, but can be used to encourage the ants to transfer to a new nest, and direct sunlight must be avoided or the heat could become lethal. A temperature of 20-30°C is suitable for full activity but it can drop below this at night. In winter it is convenient to put nests in a refrigerator running at about 5°C, so that feeding is unnecessary, but the water needs to be kept topped up. Food can be sugar solution plus prey, for which any small dead insect can be tried. The queen pupae of any common ant are the most convenient food and can be stored in an airtight container in a deep-freeze. Prey can be inserted through a hole in the top of the nest (normally closed by a rubber bung) and the sugar may be placed as a droplet over a hole too small for an ant head to go through. The inside of the nest must not become contaminated with sugar or excess prey.

Nests of *L.flavus* and *F.fusca* have been kept for a dozen years under these conditions.

PREVIOUS RECORDING OF SURREY ANTS

British ants, their life-history and classification by H. St.J. K. Donisthorpe (2nd edition, 1927) is quite rightly the most well-known book on the natural history of British ants. It also lists records of the less common species under the names in use at that time.

There are surprisingly few records from Surrey and this is mainly because only a few entomologists worked on ants, but also because travel was more restrictive then. Many of Donisthorpe's own records are from Box Hill, "Weybridge" and "Woking" in Surrey, and notably "Beaulieu Road" in the New Forest – all easy trips on the railway from London. He includes records made by other collectors, one of whom, Saunders, was even less mobile – all his listed Surrey records are from "Woking" or "Chobham". It is often not easy to decide which precise location was meant, and there may also be doubt about the species. For example, *Lasius meridionalis* was presumably included in *L.umbratus*, and similarly *L.psammophilus* in *L.alienus*, in these sandy habitats.

There are too few records from that time to conclude very much about changes of distribution, but, looking at Britain as a whole, there is a persistence of species except where habitats have been destroyed by urbanisation or a change to recreational use. In Surrey, *Tetramorium*, *Myrmica lobicornis*, "*Lasius alienus*" and *Formica sanguinea* were recorded from Shirley, but no more recent records have been found. *Tetramorium* is an excellent indicator species for dry heath and was even recorded in London, on Hampstead Heath in 1895.

Lack of heathland management has apparently resulted in the loss of "*L.alienus*" and the exceptionally rare *F.rufibarbis* from Reigate Heath and the loss of *F.rufibarbis*, *F.sanguinea*, *L.psammophilus*, *Tetramorium* and *M.sulcinodis* from the Weybridge area.

The only species added to the Surrey list since 1927 have been *M.schencki*, *M.karavajevi*, *Anergates*, *L.brunneus*, *F.picea* and the recently split species of *Lasius* – *L.platythorax*, *L.psammophilus* and *L.meridionalis*.

Very few lists of records for the whole county of Surrey have been published, but records of *F.rufa* up to 1964 and *F.sanguinea* up to 1965 by K.E.J.Barrett and J.C.Felton attempt to cover the whole county. They show remarkable similarity to those produced here – probably because these species are relatively easy to find and are not critically confined to rare habitats. Both readily move their nests to suitable local sites.

LIST OF RECORDERS

G.W.Allen	J.S.Denton	A.J.Halstead	R.K.A.Morris	A.J.Rundle
D.W.Baldock	N.J.Donnithorne	R.D.Hawkins	D.Oliver	P.Skidmore
J.P.Brock	M.Edwards	P.R.Harvey	J.A.Owen	J.A.White
G.A.Collins	S.J.Falk	P.J.Hodge	M.S.Parsons	
A.S.Davidson	M.G.Fox	R.A.Jones	C.W.Plant	

ACKNOWLEDGEMENTS

It is a pleasure to thank many people who have contributed valuable help in the publication of this book, including the list of recorders. However, several people need special mention for making the completed book possible.

David Baldock, as well as contributing many records, prepared the species distribution maps and provided some necessary encouragement to start me working on it. Graham Collins drew the diagrams, and additional photographs were provided by Andy Callow and David Element. Steve Gschmeissner and Paul Pearce-Kelly supplied the scanning-electron-micrographs.

Roger Hawkins, as has become usual with this atlas series, proof-read the written material at two stages and added valuable comments, while Clare Windsor prepared the book for publication alongside Alistair Kirk, representing the publisher Surrey Wildlife Trust.

The species distribution maps were prepared using the Dmap computer program written by Dr Alan Morton of Imperial College at Silwood Park.

RECORDING SCHEMES

The Bees, Wasps and Ants Recording Scheme (BWARS), operated under the auspices of the Biological Records Centre, CEH Monks Wood, Abbots Ripton, Huntingdon, Cambs PE28 2LS, gives members a starter pack to help with their recording together with species profiles and provisional atlases showing national distribution. See the website: www.bwars.com

Of the county-based biological records centres, two cover Vice-county 17:

Surrey Biological Records Centre, c/o Surrey Wildlife Trust, School Lane, Pirbright, Woking, Surrey GU24 0JN. Email sybrc@surreywt.org.uk

Greenspace Information for Greater London, Skyline House, 200 Union Street, London SE1 0LW. Email gigl@wildlondon.org.uk

EXPLANATION OF THE SPECIES ACCOUNTS

Surrey, in spite of being in crowded south-eastern Britain, is still one of the best counties for number of ant species, since it has 30 out of the 42 native species currently recorded from the British Isles. The status of these species is well worth mapping, both for general interest and to assist conservation in the future.

The localised nests make mapping, habitat description and analysis of conservation requirements much more straightforward with ants than with most other animals.

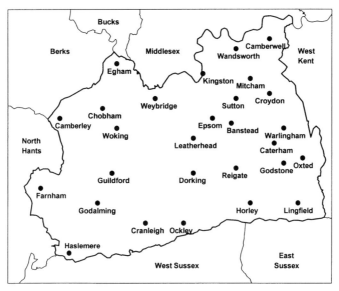

Surrey (Vice-county 17) in relation to bordering vice-counties

Vice-county 17 is used as the recording area, and the records are plotted in a grid of 2km squares for uniformity with other volumes in the atlas series, although ant nests could be more precisely mapped using the Global Positioning System. Local extinctions are likely to be missed with such a coarse grid, and habitat specialisation would be detected better if detailed local conditions were mapped.

Dispersing winged queens might be collected well away from a suitable habitat and, where these are found in squares with no nest records, a distinctive symbol is used. On the other hand, workers found without discovering a nest are given full record status. No weight can be given to dense well-established populations, as opposed to isolated nests with low numbers of workers.

Some of the gaps in the distribution maps are the result of inadequate recording, since some ants, for example *Lasius flavus*, may well be found wherever grass grows in a sunny site, if not too dry. Other gaps are real and indicate habitat differences which are dealt with under "Habitats and Conservation" (page 17) or in the species accounts.

The lengths quoted are for workers.

Four subfamilies of the family Formicidae are represented in Britain and these are described in the following order: Formicinae, with 13 species currently recorded in Surrey, Myrmicinae with 15, Dolichoderinae with one, and Ponerinae with one.

An unconventional sequence is used here so that a familiar and unexceptional species can be dealt with first.

KEY TO DISTRIBUTION MAP SYMBOLS

+ Records pre-1900

○ Records 1900-1949

◉ Records 1950-1984

● Records 1985-2005

× Records of queens only

FAMILY FORMICIDAE

Subfamily Formicinae

This subfamily includes two genera currently found in Britain: *Lasius* and *Formica*. It is characterised by having only one segment in the waist, no sting, and a terminal orifice in females which is circular with a ring of hairs. Formic acid is found in the aggressive secretions of some species of Formicinae, but is not produced by other ants. The pupae are usually enclosed in cocoons. Both genera have sometimes been divided and given extra names, but these are rejected here in favour of stable names and familiar large groups. A third genus, *Camponotus* (a very large world-wide group), was present in England in the last interglacial period, but apparently failed to recolonise this country after the ice receded.

Genus *Lasius*

Males are of similar size to workers whereas the queens are larger – very much larger in most of the species – and can carry the males when flying on their conspicuous mating flights. Formic acid is a minor constituent of the secretions of a few *Lasius* species, but many of them smell of quite different substances. Larvae are present in the nests through the winter. Those species which are subterranean are yellow and have reduced eyes, but those which forage above ground are dark brown or black. This dark pigment might be either camouflage or protection from radiation, but this has not been established by research.

Lasius niger (Linnaeus, 1758)   PLATES 1, 11, 14   The Garden Black Ant

Status in Surrey: Abundant in sunny medium-dry sites

Length: 4-5mm

The familiar "black ant" lives in gardens, under pavements and also in many sunny rural habitats. It is actually dark brown and is easily the most frequently seen British species, often entering houses. The very driest and hottest habitats can be too extreme for it, and it is replaced there by other species of *Lasius*. Waterlogged sites are also not suitable.

Healthy nests are always under

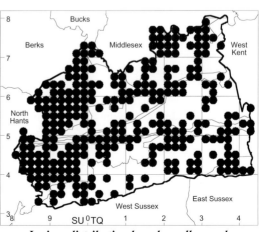

L.niger distribution based on all records

an unshaded bare surface which can be paving or stones or a friable mound made by the ants from moist soil. The nests, like those of most ant species, do not survive under heavy grazing, but the grazing of Soay sheep, used to manage a research plot at Englefield Green, allowed excellent survival.

Foraging is normally above ground on herbs and trees, but the tending of subterranean aphids is also quite usual. The ant avoids direct exposure to sunlight, where there is a choice, and may make earthen covers over well-used trails or up stems over colonies of aphids.

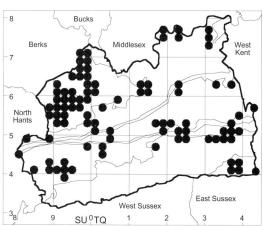

Mating flights take place in July or August, with synchronous take-off over areas many miles wide. The synchrony is not as good as it appears, for nests under pavements may well fly before those in rural situations. However, there are reports of traffic being halted by the enormous numbers which sometimes come down in local air

L.niger distribution based on recent positive identifications using queens or good series of workers

currents, and these may be ten miles from the nearest populations capable of producing such numbers. There is little other information on the distances travelled by flying ants, but they do fly upwards and may get into the high-altitude cross-currents which could disperse them longer distances. High temperatures, coinciding with high humidity, trigger the flights which can occur at the end of a very hot dry spell when rain falls overnight (e.g. 23rd July 1967), as well as the usual circumstances of hot thundery weather after a cooler period.

The newly fertilised queens choose bare ground, posssibly by detecting the infra-red rays given off by hot surfaces, and may be collected at densities of more than ten per square metre. This is a far higher density than mature nests can achieve, since these establish exclusive foraging territories of four metres radius through boundary wars in spring. Each nest normally has only one functional queen, but produces several hundred alate queens per year. Since a nest can persist for at least ten years, the overall odds against the success of new nest-founding queens are therefore more than a thousand to one.

Each queen attempts to found a new nest alone, sealed in an earthen tubular cell, and tiny new workers can be produced in the first autumn. Their success is negligible in the shade or in areas with previously established nests, where the new ants are killed by the foragers from existing nests.

Nests are more easily reared in captivity if queens are given pupae of their own species, but they do not rear the brood of sibling species. Experience of this behaviour foreshadowed the subsequent description of *L.platythorax* as a new species.

Almost all squares on the Surrey map would probably show a record of *L.niger* if we had more recorders and its identification was less problematic.

It is widespread in Britain and Ireland, but less generally distributed in the north where most records are from low altitudes and further confirmation of its identity is needed from many sites now that *L.platythorax* has been recognised as a distinct species.

Lasius platythorax Seifert, 1991   PLATES 1, 11, 14

Status in Surrey: Common and shade-tolerant

Length: 4-5mm

This species is very similar to *L.niger* and was confused with it until recently, despite being widespread in occurrence and distinctive in queen morphology. These queens have a much shallower thorax, relative to their size, than other species of *Lasius*, but they are otherwise easily confusable with *L.niger*. None were found when collecting

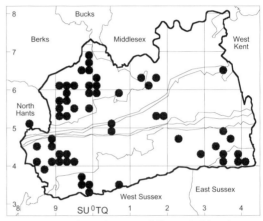

hundreds of *L.niger* queens for research, because they choose a different habitat for nest foundation. They settle among vegetation and enter crevices in bark or rotten wood. The shallow thorax is presumably an adaptation to help them get into narrow gaps. The workers of *L.platythorax* are blacker and have longer hairs than those of *L.niger*, but, to be confident of their identity, comparison with workers already collected with identified queens is necessary. Dead specimens of workers in a collection look very similar indeed. The clypeus of *L.niger* has denser and shorter hairs than that of *L.platythorax*, but these need a microscope to examine them and are often difficult to see.

The general biology of *L.platythorax* is otherwise similar to *L.niger*, as far as we have observed, except that it is much more tolerant of shade. A nest found near Juniper Hall in fallen logs was completely shaded by trees, but it had alate queens so was obviously mature and successful. However, the ant is also common in dead wood in sunny situations.

In Surrey this species is abundant on damp heaths with decaying pine stumps, but also occurs in the major woodlands and other habitats with dead wood. Perhaps it represents the final stage of ecological succession, for it is well adapted to invade tree-fall sites after the other species of *Lasius* have dominated the earlier stages of plant succession. However, one nest at Thursley Common was found in a peaty hump near a bog in full sun. This species is potentially susceptible to parasitism by the *L.umbratus* group of species, so ant succession could have formed a full cycle before human domination of the environment.

Those myrmecophiles recorded with "*L.niger*", before the separation of *L.platythorax*, need to have their hosts carefully identified in future.

L.platythorax is still under-recorded, but it begins to look likely that in Surrey it is more abundant than *L.niger* in rural areas (except heaths), while *L.niger* is the more abundant ant in urban areas. Its British distribution is not yet well recorded, but it occurs on Cumbrian coastal sites as far north as Allonby, and in Scotland there is a definite record from Tentsmuir Point on the Tay estuary.

Lasius alienus (Förster, 1850)

Status in Surrey: Local in dry, sunny chalk grassland

Length: 3.5-4.5mm

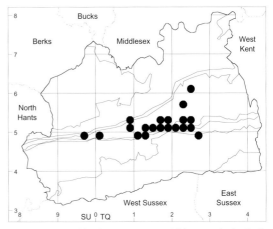

This small black ant of chalky districts is confusable with *L.niger* or *L.platythorax*, but lacks their standing hairs, especially on its tibiae and scapes. There are only one or two hairs on the back of the propodeum. It replaces *L.niger* and *L.flavus* on the hottest and driest parts of chalk downs, where it is locally abundant in very short or stony grassland. In general appearance it is slightly smaller and at least as black as *L.niger*. Old records include some for *L.psammophilus*, which has similarly hairless appendages but was only recently recognised as a distinct species living on sandy heaths.

This ant is very similar in general biology to *L.niger*, but is less seen above ground. It tends coccids as well as aphids in their underground colonies on these dry sites.

The mating flights are later than those of *L.niger*, usually in September, and the queens choose patches of bare soil to start their nests.

It is a southern species in Britain which is present on many limestone hills and non-sandy coastal sites.

Lasius psammophilus Seifert, 1992

Status in Surrey: Local on dry heaths

Length: 3.5-5mm

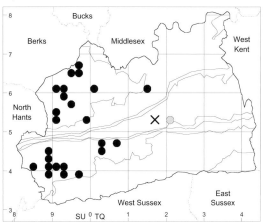

Until recently this ant was included within *L.alienus*, so all early records could refer to either species. The clearest distinguishing character needs microscopic examination and is the presence of hairs down the rear lateral angles of the propodeum in this species. These rear angles are usually bare in *L.alienus*, but there may be one or two hairs present. Checking a series of specimens is valuable, in case of abrasion or adhesion of hairs to the surface. There are usually some paler brown workers present in nests of *L.psammophilus*, because callow colouration persists longer than usual. This is also a less active species than *L.alienus*, but these latter features are too subjective to be relied on for identification. This ant is much less aggressive to an observer than is *L.niger*.

This is a good indicator species for dry heath in Surrey, but elsewhere it occurs in other sandy habitats (e.g. coastal dunes). It survives severe fires well. Sampling a transect up Shrike Hill at Thursley Common showed a strong zonation of heathland ants, with this species occupying the highest level, *Tetramorium* on the slope facing south-west, and *L.platythorax* at the bottom (with one *L.niger* nest in an open patch). The slope is presumably the hottest, best drained zone, and the bottom is the wettest with dead stumps, logs and some shading by trees.

Habitat difference should not be used for identification, in case there are exceptions which have not been recognised after the recent division of the species. Headley Heath had this species in the 1960s (within easy flying distance to *L.alienus* on a chalk down 200m away), but it has not been found there since the growth of gorse, bracken and scrub has produced too much shading. It is, however, remarkable that *L.psammophilus* is not recorded from chalk downs, because most heath species occur in both these hot habitats, for instance *Formica cunicularia* and *Myrmica sabuleti*. Even *Tetramorium* and *Tapinoma* occur on hot, coastal, non-sandy sites in Britain and are widespread on grassland in the hotter parts of Europe.

Mating flights are late and occur in September or even October. There are very few records of habitat choice by the queens, but they have been seen to alight on parked cars and tarmac surfaces, so presumably the choice of bare areas is normal.

It is difficult to see how the queens of this interesting pair of species can choose their different habitats without apparent error and within overlapping geographical ranges – remembering that *L.psammophilus* chooses grassland when on dunes and *L.alienus* is only recorded from hot grassland sites which are not sandy. Perhaps all the queens landing on the wrong soil type die without succeeding in rearing colonies? 99.9% die in any case, before producing their own sexual female progeny, so very powerful natural selection is available and could therefore be acting either on very small genetic differences or on valid, reproductively isolated species. However we must apply both species names, at least until we know better – if we do not retain the separate names we never will know better!

L.psammophilus has been recorded from sandy sites in southern Britain and the midlands, e.g. Hartlebury Common in Worcestershire. Records of "*L.alienus*" from similar habitats in the north require confirmation, but are presumably *L.psammophilus*.

Lasius brunneus (Latreille, 1798)   PLATE 3   **The Brown Tree Ant**

Status in Surrey: Local in woodland and parkland

Length: 3.5-4.5mm

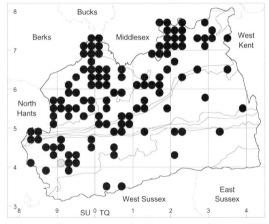

This is a distinctly bicoloured species that lives on old trees. The thorax is paler than the brown head and gaster of a darker neutral colour. The ant is usually seen foraging on tree trunks, where it is non-aggressive and shows avoidance behaviour when disturbed, for it rapidly hides in a crevice. Sometimes *L.niger* is misidentified as this species when found on tree trunks, but *L.brunneus* does not have the hairy appendages of the common species.

The nests are in dead heartwood or thick bark of standing trees, especially oaks. They have also been recorded in many other species of trees and occasionally in man-made wooden structures. A wooden bridge over a stream at Horsell Common was weakened by its workings, with concurrent rot and other insect damage, and the bridge eventually collapsed under a load. A brown frass is exuded from cracks and gives away the location of nests, but *L.brunneus* is not the only creature to do this.

The distribution of this insect is unusual. It is abundant in north-west Surrey and Berkshire with scattered records from neighbouring counties in the south-east and also in central England. Most records are from old parkland, Windsor and Richmond being typical park habitats, but it can be found in old trees much more generally. It is, oddly enough, unrecorded from the New Forest area or further west, while Donisthorpe recorded it only from Berkshire in the 1920s. Is it spreading from a small introduction or has it simply been overlooked in the past? It is inconspicuous and certainly under-recorded, but Donisthorpe was an excellent observer and did not find it in several sites where it has since been found abundantly.

L.*niger* workers with queen

L.*niger*: earth 'tent' around
ragwort aphids

L.*niger* in nest: the larval gut contents are visible

Snail *Helix aspersa* producing mucus
in response to L.*niger* attack

L.*niger* tending black rose aphids

L.*platythorax* with aphids

Lasius niger (**Garden Black Ant**) and *Lasius platythorax*

PLATE 1

L.flavus nests in old pasture

L.flavus adults with eggs

L.flavus winged queens emerging for
mating flight

L.flavus adults with queen cocoons and larvae

L.flavus with larvae and aphids on
underground grass stems

L.flavus with aphid eggs overwintering

Lasius flavus (Yellow Meadow Ant)

PLATE 2

L.brunneus adult worker in crack of bark

L.brunneus nest in oak heartwood

L.brunneus nest in dead pine

L.meridionalis queen with workers

L.meridionalis carton nest

L.meridionalis queen, newly flown, carrying
worker of host species *(L.platythorax)*

Lasius brunneus (Brown Tree Ant) and Lasius meridionalis

PLATE 3

Mixed nest of *L.meridionalis* and parasitic *L.fuliginosus*

L.fuliginosus with prey

10cm long part of *L.fuliginosus*
nest carton

Lasius fuliginosus (Jet Black Ant)

PLATE 4

F.rufa nest in open woodland

F.rufa trail

F.rufa nest with holes made by green woodpecker

F.rufa workers

Formica rufa (Wood Ant)

PLATE 5

F.rufa with fly as prey

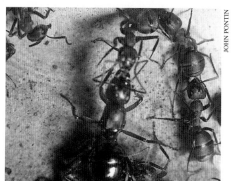

F.rufa worker feeding queen

F.rufa: massed sunbathing in spring

F.rufa with tiny *Formicoxenus nitidulus* ants

Formica rufa (Wood Ant)

PLATE 6

F.sanguinea with *F.fusca* slaves

F.sanguinea gynandromorph

F.sanguinea queen

Female *F.rufibarbis* 'calling'

Copulating pair of *F.rufibarbis*

Ideal hot, sandy habitat for *F.rufibarbis*

Formica sanguinea (Slavemaker) and Formica rufibarbis

PLATE 7

M.ruginodis feeding on nectar

M.ruginodis with winged males

M.ruginodis with pupae and larvae of varying ages

A rare variety of *M.sabuleti* with
unusually shaped hairs

M.ruginodis tending aphids

Myrmica ruginodis and Myrmica sabuleti

PLATE 8

Leptothorax acervorum nest in
dead pine wood

Stenamma workers with brood

Myrmecina graminicola attracted to wet
area (firebrick) in artificial nest

Anergates queen egg-laying in
Tetramorium nest

Tetramorium caespitum larvae and alate pupae

Anergates atratulus alate queen

Tetramorium caespitum with *Anergates* alate queen

***Leptothorax acervorum*, *Stenamma*, *Myrmecina graminicola*,
Tetramorium caespitum and *Anergates***

PLATE 9

Tapinoma erraticum with larvae

Ponera coarctata

Ant mimic – *Myrmarachne formicaria*,
a jumping spider

Ant mimic – nymph of *Alydus calcaratus*, a bug

***Tapinoma erraticum, Ponera coarctata* and two ant mimics**

PLATE 10

Lasius niger with (left) pupa and (right) adult of *Plebejus argus*, the Silver-studded Blue butterfly

Lasius platythorax with larva of *Microdon analis*, a hoverfly

Tetramorium with winged and non-winged
Paracletus cimiciformis aphids

Myrmecophiles – butterfly, hoverfly, aphid

PLATE 11

Clytra quadripunctata beetle larva
on *Formica rufa* nest

Lasius fuliginosus with *Amphotis marginata*,
a beetle

Formica sanguinea with larva of *Lomechusa strumosa*, a beetle

Lasius flavus associate:
Claviger testaceus,
a beetle

Myrmica ruginodis with *Platyarthrus hoffmannseggi*,
a small blind woodlouse

Myrmecophiles – beetles and woodlouse

PLATE 12

Pirbright ranges – wet and dry heathland benefits a wide variety of ant species.

Thursley National Nature Reserve – ants thrive in the unshaded soil left after burning.
Left: ideal conditions 2 years after a fire. Right: 6 years later, now unsuitable for heathland ants.

Denbies hillside – a high temperature habitat.
Left: the turfed clay slope. Right: the chalk scarp (damaged by the trampling of ponies).

Ant habitats

PLATE 13

Queens of (above) *Lasius platythorax* and (below) *Lasius niger*

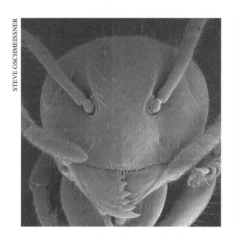

Clypeal hairs of (left) *Lasius platythorax* and (right) *Lasius niger*

Formica sanguinea showing
emarginate clypeus

Thorax of *Formica rufibarbis* queen

Ants – diagnostic features: *Lasius* and *Formica* species

PLATE 14

Anterior of *Formica rufibarbis* showing prothoracic hairs

Head of *Myrmica rubra*

Head of *Myrmica sulcinodis*

Propodeum of *Myrmica ruginodis*

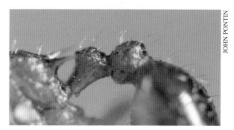

Petiole shape of *Myrmica scabrinodis*

Ants – diagnostic features: *Formica* and *Myrmica* species

PLATE 15

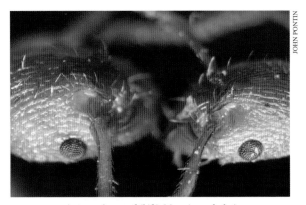

Antenna bases of (left) *Myrmica sabuleti*
and (right) *Myrmica scabrinodis*

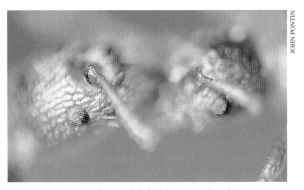

Antenna bases of (left) *Myrmica schencki*
and (right) *Myrmica lobicornis*

Ponera coarctata

Ants – diagnostic features: *Myrmica* and *Ponera* species

PLATE 16

Regrettably, it is generally the case that there are insufficient old ant records to plot changes in range comparable with the very interesting changes recorded for butterflies in Britain.

A very large aphid, *Stomaphis*, has very long mouthparts which can penetrate tree bark at the bottom of grooves in the bark. It is often associated with *L.brunneus*, but little else has been recorded as a food source in Britain. Foraging is not conspicuous in the day, but on warm nights many more ants can be seen by torchlight on tree trunks.

This species is much more difficult than other *Lasius* to culture in captivity, although newly mated queens will rear their initial brood very easily. It clearly needs some factor that is present in dead wood, and further research may reveal unusual feeding requirements. Another possible problem for research is its lack of resistance to infestations of mites in artificial nests, when compared with other ants (except *Leptothorax*). This is probably because it lacks defensive chemicals in order to remain undetected by its enemies in natural situations.

The mating flights occur earlier than for most *Lasius*, and the alates are sometimes caught in moth traps during June and early July.

Lasius flavus (Fabricius, 1782)   PLATE 2   **The Yellow Meadow Ant**

Status in Surrey: Abundant in pasture

Length: 3-5mm

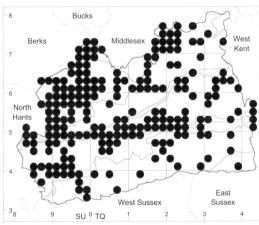

This is probably the most abundant ant in Britain, but it is seldom seen because it is subterranean. However, its nests are the conspicuous plant-covered mounds common in old pasture, for it is unusual in being able to persist under heavy grazing by large herbivores. It has reduced eyes and is yellow, except very large workers (>5mm) which are browner, queens which are dark brown with a yellow underside to the gaster, and males which are black.

The mounds increase in size with age, and if we can find sufficient examples of known-age pasture to produce a good regression analysis, it may be possible to use the largest mounds to assess the age of other sites. The largest known in Surrey are on Staines Moor (not included on the map because, although it is now in Surrey, it is not quite in vice-county 17). They have an above-ground volume of 180 litres, and a litre per year of age is a reasonable estimate from the few well-known examples. The mounds are made by the ants carrying up soil particles and placing them on the mound surface, usually at night and when the soil is moist. More than a litre a year can be deposited on top of a large nest, but the excavated soil settles so that the net increase in height is less than a centimetre per year. This can be estimated by placing a thin layer of coloured aquarium gravel on the surface of the nest, with its particles too large to be carried by a single ant, and measuring the depth of this layer several years later. Mounds are solaria, and the brood is moved around to allow warming by the sun from different directions during the course of the day. The flora on the mounds frequently differs from the surrounding grassland, and this may be the result of different temperature, dryness, or the composition of soil carried up from a lower level.

On Staines Moor each nest has an underground territory of around 1.5 metres radius, and the ants have a mean density of roughly 2,500 per square metre. Supporting them are subterranean aphids at a similar density. Both the ants and the aphids have been counted in extracted core-samples of soil.

L.flavus also occurs in gardens, but in mown lawns it cannot build mounds. In very dry sites, on chalk downs, it is replaced by *L.alienus*. It is also absent from meadows which are flooded for more than a few days at a time, and such flooding restricts its distribution on Staines Moor to the drier parts.

Mating flights are typically in July, but can be delayed by unsuitable weather. In the very cool wet autumn of 1956 no flights were made in many parts of England, and the alates in the nests did not survive into 1957. This species usually flies with the later flights of *L.niger*, resulting in similarly high densities of fertile queens choosing bare areas. Small patches of earth, such as molehills, may be found to contain a dozen of these queens, which frequently group together for colony foundation. Mature nests usually contain only one queen, but occasionally two functional queens have been found in a nest. Egg-laying queens of all *Lasius* species become swollen with eggs (physogastric) and can then be recognised as fully functional egg-laying queens.

This species could well be recorded throughout Surrey in any suitable patch of grass. It has been recorded throughout the British Isles except the outermost northern islands.

Lasius umbratus (Nylander, 1846)

Status in Surrey: Shade-tolerant, but inadequately recorded

Length: 4-6mm

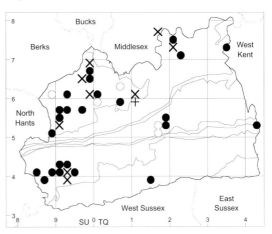

This ant is clear yellow, larger and not as variable in size as *L.flavus* in the worker caste, but the sexuals are dark brown. It too is sub-terranean, but is shade-tolerant with nests in rotting wood. These are usually in damp woodland, but sometimes in gardens where the ant is normally overlooked until it is dug up, along with its associated aphids on plant roots.

The queens of this and the two following species of *Lasius* are relatively small compared to *L.flavus*. They are temporary parasites of "black" *Lasius* such as *L.niger*. Their heads are large (at least as wide as the thorax) and their gasters are smaller because they do not need large food reserves. However, their wing area is as large as that of non-parasitic species and they can probably disperse much further in search of hosts.

After casting their wings, the queens of *L.umbratus* (and *L.meridionalis*) search the ground until they find a worker of the host species, which they then grasp – its smell may help them to enter the nests of the host. In captivity, nests can be reared with *L.niger* if they are given callow (non-aggressive) workers, but otherwise they are usually killed. There are very few records of mixed nests in the field, and more records of these are needed to establish which species are the normal hosts.

The nests consist of irregular cells, made of wood and soil fragments, called "carton". The continuous activity maintains a higher than ambient temperature within the pupal chambers, and insulation is provided by the cellular construction inside a thick layer of wood and soil. The species is, therefore, easily tolerant of full shade.

This ant is undoubtedly under-recorded in Surrey and, judging by the numbers of queens seen on the ground after a mating flight, it is actually quite a common species, but not as numerous as *L.niger* or *L.flavus*. These flights occur from July to September, and the alates are sometimes caught in the mercury-vapour light-traps used to attract moths.

There are scattered records of this species from throughout the British Isles except northern Scotland and northern Ireland.

Lasius meridionalis (Bondroit, 1920) PLATES 3, 4

Status in Surrey: Local, shade-tolerant on heathland

Length: 4-5.5mm

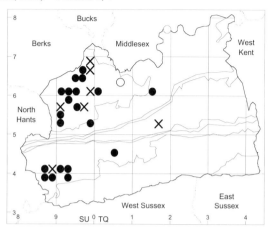

This ant was previously known in Britain as *L.rabaudi*. It is very similar to *L.umbratus* in its appearance and biology, but is slightly more amber-yellow and has flattened scapes which are most obvious in queens. The workers require careful comparison for certain identification. The ant is usually found on dry heaths where it makes carton nests in buried wood which survive fires easily. It is also tolerant of shade and persists when overgrown by bracken, gorse, scrub or tall grasses. In wet summers, temporary earth mounds may be built around grass tussocks when the alates are present and ready to fly.

The normal host could well be *L.psammophilus*, since mixed nests have been recorded at Oxshott, Chobham and Pirbright. However, the queens also attempt to enter nests of *L.platythorax* and may be found carrying workers of either of these species or of *L.niger.* The habit of *L.platythorax* of nesting in dead wood could be valuable as a basis for the carton nests of *L.meridionalis*.

Root aphids are tended, and aphid eggs have been recorded in nests, as they are with *L.flavus.*

The queens are very numerous after a flight and the species may well be much more abundant than the few records of nests would suggest.

All British records are from the southern half of England, and also from both north and south Wales.

Lasius mixtus (Nylander, 1846)

Status in Surrey: Inadequately recorded

Length: 3.5-4.5mm

This is a third temporarily parasitic yellow *Lasius*, but with clear differences from the previous two. It is bare of standing hairs on its appendages, and the queens differ in their behaviour. Mating flights occur in August and September and, later on, the young queens may be found in numbers under stones next to nests of *L.flavus*. They can survive there until the

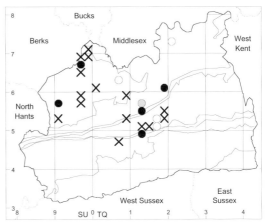

following spring, and it is possible that *L.flavus* is the normal host, although, perhaps not surprisingly, mixed nests have not been recorded. The queens of *L.mixtus* have also been found with *L.alienus* and *L.brunneus*, and, since several of the few nest records are from chalk downs, it appears more likely that *L.alienus* is the usual host. Donisthorpe found nests in dead roots of juniper, but they must be more usual in other underground wood. In captivity, the solitary queens (unlike those of the previous two species) sometimes lay eggs, but do not rear them.

This ant is definitely under-recorded. The alates can be found anywhere in Surrey and have been collected in moth-traps, but recent nest records are almost non-existent.

Specimens named as this species, because they have few or no tibial hairs, should be checked by a specialist because there are other similar species which might be recorded in Britain.

The available records suggest a general distribution in Britain and Ireland, but they are few and far between.

Lasius fuliginosus (Latreille, 1798)   PLATES 4, 12   **The Jet Black Ant**

Status in Surrey: Widespread in old habitats

Length: 4-6.5mm

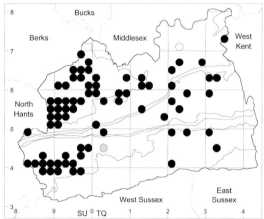

This is a very interesting, shiny, jet black species which forages above ground along its own scent-trails. It possesses a diagnostic alarm-signalling smell which, once experienced, will always identify it. Dead specimens, especially old faded ones, are best identified by the concave rear margin of the head.

Nests are large and are made of blackish carton placed either inside dead wood or in soil under the base of tree trunks. A high temperature in the pupal chamber (over 30°C in summer) is maintained by metabolism of the excess sugar obtained from aphid honeydew. Woody plants are needed for finding both aphids and prey, but nests may occur in any habitat where there are trees or bushes. Heating of the nest by the sun is completely unnecessary.

Because almost all foraging is above ground, the intake of food can be measured by counting the incoming ants on their scent trails, weighing a sample of individuals replete with honeydew, and collecting a sample of the prey carried in. During a student project at Englefield Green, almost 1500 ants were counted carrying honeydew into their nest in 15 minutes, but only 120 carrying prey (mostly non-myrmecophilous aphids). At this rate a kilo of honeydew could be collected in three days! It is a mystery how ants can store honeydew and insect blood in their crops for periods which are normally long enough for fermentation. *L.fuliginosus* is also unusual in licking sap from damaged tree buds in spring when nutrients are easily obtained in this way.

Alates are reared by May, and several flights may be made from each nest between May and October. New nests are founded by queens parasitising *L.umbratus* or *L.meridionalis* (and possibly *L.mixtus*) – nests of *L.fuliginosus* mixed with these other species have been recorded. Normally there is only one queen per mature nest, but when the M3 was being made several nests were doomed to destruction in its path, so these were excavated and one of them had five physogastric (egg-bearing) queens. It is therefore possible that nests could be multiplied by division of multi-queened nests, and this could explain the groups of nests occasionally found.

There is a clear ecological succession from pioneer "black" *Lasius*, such as *L.niger,* through shade-tolerant *L.umbratus* or *L.meridionalis*, then finally to tree-loving *L.fuliginosus*. This has become a compulsory sequence because the invasion of habitats already occupied by an aggressive Lasius is difficult, unless the replacing queens are evolved to do so.

Intraspecific competition between nests is also avoided by this strategy, because the invaded nests are already territorially spaced.

All of Surrey, except the fully urbanised parts, is suitable for this species, but it is not usually common in disturbed habitats. It takes perhaps 20 years for the ant succession to get to this stage, but plant succession has been speeded up too much by our activities for the temporarily parasitic species to fit in easily.

L.fuliginosus has been recorded from most of England, the Isle of Man and the southern half of Ireland. It is easily found, so this distribution is likely to be realistic.

Genus *Formica*

All species forage above ground during the day (possibly also at night if warm enough) and are dark-coloured with larger eyes compared with those of *Lasius*. They are more resistant to desiccation than other British ants. There is no over-wintering brood, and the males are as big as the queens. Mating does not take place in flight, but on plants or other raised surfaces. Males fly to the mating sites, which are near to the females' nest, and then the females fly away to found new nests or become accepted in old nests.

The only ants which produce large quantities of formic acid (up to 22% of body weight) are in this genus, and only *Formica rufa*, of the Surrey species, squirts it into the air when disturbed. One should avoid getting this in one's eyes. All species tend arboreal and/or herb-living aphids, take prey (including non-myrmecophilous aphids), and use floral or extra-floral nectaries.

Formica rufa Linnaeus, 1761   PLATES 5, 6, 12   The Wood Ant

Status in Surrey: Frequent in open woodland

Length: 4.5-10mm

In Surrey, the nest is diagnostic. The large accumulation of vegetable material, often more than a foot high, enables maintenance of an elevated brood temperature because its insulation retains the metabolic heat of the ants' activity. Several other *Formica* species, not at present recorded from the county, make similar nests, so specimens should be retained in

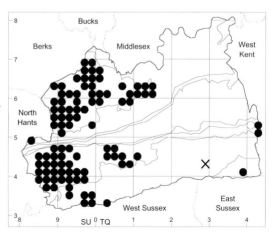

case expert identification becomes important. In the spring, the ants mass on the nest surface to be warmed in the sun, but shade is tolerated for the rest of the year. They therefore nest in deciduous woodland or at the edge of dense conifer plantations. Very large numbers of workers can be found in one nest – several hundred thousand must be common – and perhaps about a hundred queens can be found in the sun-bathing masses in spring.

New nests are usually formed by large groups of workers, along with some queens, migrating out from parent nests to new sites which are often in rotting stumps or logs. Workers frequently carry nestmates to new sites.

It has been suggested that queens, after mating, attempt to parasitise nests of *F.fusca*, but there are no supposed records in Surrey, substantiated by known specimens, of nests of *F.rufa* mixed with other ants. They are very bad colonisers of isolated new woodlands, and all the records are from old habitats. Conservation is therefore especially important. (The closely related *F.pratensis*, which needs higher temperatures, has become extinct in Britain during the last 50 years.)

Wood Ants are legally protected in some countries, and related species have been introduced to new areas in attempts to control tree pests, so the loss of the species from a site may not be final. Isolated introductions are, however, very vulnerable to predation by the Green Woodpecker and "anting" by other birds.

Alates are produced early in the year, sometimes as early as March but usually later, with mating behaviour in late May or early June. Queens can fly at least a mile and on one occasion a group of 20+ was found at Chobham Common under a piece of metal rubbish. This group acquired stray workers from a distant nest and persisted to form a small new nest. It is not known if this record is really unique or represents normal behaviour.

Foragers follow conspicuous trails to known food sources, but are not dependent on them, and many lone workers may be found up to 50 metres from the nest.

F.rufa is widespread in west Surrey with scattered colonies elsewhere, but apparently only survives in east Surrey at Limpsfield Chart and on Blackberry Road, Felcourt. It is absent from the chalk and from most clay woodland.

The most northerly records from England are from south Cumbria, since it is replaced by similar species in cooler areas of Britain and in Ireland.

Formica sanguinea Latreille, 1798   PLATES 7, 12, 14   The Slavemaker

Status in Surrey: Frequent on heathland

Length: 6-10mm

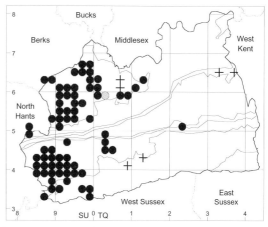

This species is superficially similar to the Wood Ant, but with more red, and it also lacks the ability to squirt formic acid into the air. It has a shallow notch in its clypeus (upper lip) and this should be checked to confirm its identity. Most nests have workers of *F.fusca*, *F.cunicularia* or even *F.rufibarbis* behaving as normally as they do with their own species.

Occasionally there are no "slaves", so *F.sanguinea* is clearly not fully dependent upon them. Nests of the slave species are raided by co-ordinated armies of *F.sanguinea* to carry off pupae which are reared or eaten. The resulting auxiliary workers are not coerced by their acquired nestmates and will attack their sisters from their parent nest if they meet. Little is known about the communication needed to coordinate an attacking army.

F.sanguinea usually inhabits heathland and nests in dead tree-stumps or logs or banks in sunny sites. Nests are often moved, perhaps because they run out of slave nests to raid, but also as the result of disturbance. As with Wood Ants, workers often carry nestmates when nests are moved. There is an exceptional nest in a woodland glade known as Botany Bay, near Chiddingfold, but several nests there have been destroyed by removal of the stumps they lived in. It is a relatively rare species in Britain and may well be mistaken for the more abundant Wood Ant and hence not actively conserved.

Alates fly in July and the newly fertilised queens are temporary social parasites of *F.fusca* or possibly other similar species.

An interesting phenomenon – bilateral gynandromorphism – is commonest in this species and has occurred in the majority of sexuals in one nest west of Pirbright. The sex determination of the body cells of insects is not under central control via hormones, as in mammals, so, if an accident at the first cell division of a fertilised ant-egg produces one diploid and one haploid cell, then the resulting adult, if it can survive, becomes half male and half female divided longitudinally down the middle. It can be a winged male on one side and a wingless worker on the other, with the halves differing in colour as well as in morphology. This phenomenon is very rare in most ant species, but, in the case of *F.sanguinea*, it is worth looking out for these striking individuals and observing their social behaviour. These gynandromorphs also occur with smaller body-portions of the male sex and the resulting mosaics are more rare.

Surrey has exceptionally large numbers of *F.sanguinea* and it is present on all but very small isolated heaths (in spite of being rated "Notable" in the Red Data Book). It is also present in other heathy areas of south-east England as far west as Dorset, but is absent from further south-west. There are isolated records from the west midlands and it is also well established in parts of the Scottish highlands – an unusually disjunct distribution.

Formica fusca Linnaeus, 1758

Status in Surrey: Common on pioneer-stage habitats

Length: 5-7mm

This is a fairly common, fast-running black species, typically without any hairs on top of its thorax. Care is needed to distinguish it from the following species of *Formica*.

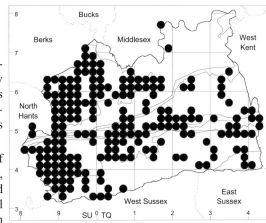

It colonises sunny pioneer stages of plant succession in many habitats, including suburban gardens, and can sometimes persist in partial shade. Nests are frequently in rotten stumps or logs, or under stones, and are readily moved after disturbance or too much shading. Workers only number up to a few hundred per nest.

The workers forage singly and retreat rapidly with little aggression when disturbed.

Mating flights occur in July, and the queens can found colonies alone without feeding themselves. Mature nests frequently have more than one queen, but the origin of these is not known.

This ant is widespread in Surrey and southern England, but there are fewer records from the north and from Ireland, where *F.lemani* is the usual black *Formica* species.

Formica cunicularia Latreille, 1798

Status in Surrey: Hot sites on chalk down or heath

Length: 5-7mm

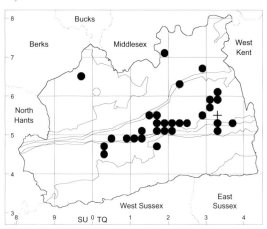

This ant is very similar to *F.fusca* in its morphology and biology, but the surface of the gaster is dull rather than silky, while the legs and thorax may be reddish. The cheeks, at least, are normally reddish, and the red colour is sometimes extensive on the trunk and legs. The ants may be much redder than the very rare *F.rufibarbis* and have been wrongly recorded as that species. There may be a few short weak standing hairs on the thorax of *F.cunicularia*, but the numerous strong bristles on the front of the trunk of *F.rufibarbis* are normally distinctive. However, it is advisable to examine several specimens in case an old abraded individual of *F.rufibarbis* is found first.

F.cunicularia needs hotter nest sites than *F.fusca*, and these are typically on chalk scarps or dry heaths. The nest may be under stones or in grass with earth built up to make a bare mound in the sun. The spider *Myrmarachne formicaria* is an excellent mimic of this ant and regularly occurs with it at Denbies Hillside.

The species occurs in the southern half of England and in both the south and north of Wales.

Formica rufibarbis Fabricius, 1793   PLATES 7, 14

Status in Surrey: Nearly extinct on hot dry heathland

Length: 5-7mm

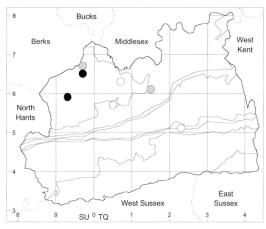

This is possibly the rarest resident animal in mainland Britain at the time of writing. We know of four nests in Surrey, one of which is captive-reared and was released in 2003. The main distinction between this ant and *F.cunicularia* is that *F.rufibarbis* has more than two hairs on top of the prothorax, where *F.cunicularia* is usually bare. When alive, *F.rufibarbis* appears to have blackish legs compared to its reddish-brown thorax, but this difference is less convincing in dead specimens in a collection. The queens are more distinctive, since the thorax of *F.rufibarbis* is red with dark patches, whereas the thorax of queen *F.cunicularia* is predominantly dark grey to black.

The very hottest sites on sandy dry heaths are needed for successful nests, and small aphid-bearing trees nearby are probably important. The workers are much more aggressive to observers than those of the previous two species.

F.rufibarbis is a common species in many parts of continental Europe, but the only other sites for it in the British Isles are on the Scillies, and all the old records are from Surrey heaths. Donisthorpe recorded numerous nests near Weybridge prior to 1920, and reported records from Reigate in 1905 and Ripley in 1908. There was one nest at Oxshott in 1964, but this was extinct in 1965. The next find was at Chobham Common in 1967, but a rubbish dump (!) was established on this site. The expansion of the pile of debris was followed by loss of the *F.rufibarbis* in September 1968, in spite of attempts to stop dumping through consultation on site with a representative of the Nature Conservancy! After this, the species was thought to be extinct until it was re-found in 1992 on Stickledown rifle range and Chobham Common, at both of which sites it still persists.

Nests may have more than one queen, but if each nest has only one, then the known Surrey population size is effectively just four individuals!

Any *Formica* with hairs on the anterior top of its thorax should be recorded and its identity checked. It could be this species, on the verge of extinction, or the rare Bog Ant, *F.picea*, if shiny black (or perhaps even the cool moorland or northern *F.lemani*, of which there is a very doubtful old record in Surrey).

Mating takes place on prominent plant stems where the alate queens "call" the males using an attractive scent (a "pheromone") which is released in response to the presence of males. This is presumably just normal courtship behaviour in *Formica*, but very few observations have been made. Nests may have more than one queen, and new nests may be set up by subdivision. In captivity, young queens easily found new nests alone, and this increases their chance of success by more than a hundred times, so this is a possible method of building up the wild populations by reintroduction. There is, however, a major snag with this approach to increasing the number of nests. Each mature nest of a *Formica* tends to produce either males or females until very old, when a few males are produced from nests previously producing females (presumably from unfertilised eggs laid by workers). The only mature nest now present at Chobham produces only females. Males have been produced at Stickledown and by a very old nest at Chobham, which has since died out, but some fertilised females were captured at Chobham in 1995-7 and nests reared in the laboratory.

Use of the range at Stickledown has prevented access at the right time to collect males. Otherwise, captive mating would appear to be a possibility. However, mating in captive containers, ranging from a conservatory to muslin cages used for moths, has so far failed because the females do not call – they spend all their time attempting to escape.

Two attempts to reintroduce captive nests at Chobham failed for unknown reasons. A third introduced nest was moved by the ants from a well-drained site to a wetter, more bare site, which was chosen by them in dry summer weather. Very low numbers have persisted there for two years and waterlogging in winter is likely to eliminate them entirely. They do not move nests when inactive at winter temperatures.

This area of Chobham Common is not ideal for the ant, since the soil has a high clay content and dense vegetation after recovery from a fire which occurred before 1990. The plant cover is mainly two grasses, *Agrostis curtisii* and *Molinia caerulea*, not the more suitable sparse heather on sandy banks. Management has been difficult and limited to scraping off the plants and surface layer of soil. This recovers much too quickly by grass seeding, and a continuous sward can develop in three or four years, whereas the ant's nests need that time to grow to reproductive age and could persist for at least another ten years if the habitat remained suitable. The bank at Stickledown has been extended, using an excavator, and the bare sandy bank produced has persisted well into a fourth year. This is potentially a much better management technique, as there is no seed-bank available for starting succession and the south-facing bank is both hot and well-drained. Slave raids by *F.sanguinea* have since become dangerous.

English Nature has funded the study of this ant as one of their Species Recovery Programmes. (The management suitable for this ant, of course, automatically favours several other rare insect species which need the same special habitat.)

Formica picea Nylander 1846   The Black Bog Ant

Status in Surrey: Very rare in *Sphagnum* bog

Length: 4.5-6mm

This ant was previously called *F.candida* and, before that, *F.transkaucasica*. It is as shiny and black as *L.fuliginosus*, but faster running and with solitary foraging like *F.fusca*. The nests are normally in quaking *Sphagnum* bogs or sometimes at the edge between these and wet heath. It can submerge itself on disturbance, but probably cannot survive long-term

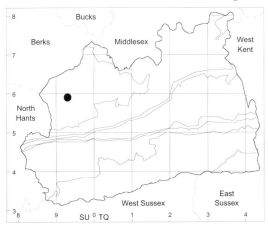

flooding. Numerous long hairs on top of the thorax distinguish it from *F.fusca*, but these can be abraded in old individuals, so several specimens should be checked if the first ones found in a bog are bare.

Apart from the unusual habitat, it is similar biologically to *F.fusca* as far as is known.

This is a rare species in Britain and was not found in Surrey until 2003, when good access to the military land around Colony Bog was permitted. Worker ants were collected on three areas of bog by Jonty Denton and Graham Collins, so it is well established here, many miles from its nearest site in the New Forest.

Subfamily Myrmicinae

This is the second of the two major subfamilies found in Britain. The ants have stings, two segments in the waist, naked pupae, and males of similar size to the winged queens. Their gasters are smooth in appearance, but the rest of their body can be coarsely roughened by irregular grooves. Such sculpture is usually termed "rugose".

Genus *Myrmica*

These species are called "Red Ants" in some literature, but so are Wood Ants in other accounts, and the name is therefore best avoided.

The eleven species found in Britain present initial problems of identification as a result of the difficulty in describing and illustrating their differences. Once these features have been correctly recognised, most of the species can actually be identified with confidence, although it is often helpful to collect several workers from each nest.

Eight species have been recorded in Surrey, six of which have medium-sized colonies, but *M.rubra* can have fairly large ones and *M.karavajevi* is a workerless parasite of other species of *Myrmica*. All are reddish-brown, medium-sized, inconspicuous foragers with relatively slow movements. Some of them show a tendency to crepuscular foraging.

Myrmica rubra (Linnaeus, 1758)   PLATES 8, 15

Status in Surrey: Local in damp, open, non-flooding sites

Length: 3.5-5mm

This species is distinguished by having spines on its propodeum which are clearly shorter than the width of the space between them, and this space being smooth without transverse furrows. It is one of the few British ants which can sting us effectively. The resulting feeling is similar to that of a stinging nettle, but soon fades. The species was previously known as *M.laevinodis*.

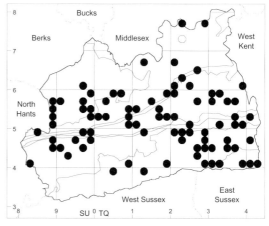

The nests do not need to be in the warmest sites and are usually found in places which remain damp, but are not flooded for more than a few days at a time. They can be extensive, with many queens, and the workers are most easily seen foraging on tall herbs where they

may be taken in sweep-nets. There are many suitable localised sites in clay districts, where stones or similar debris have been dumped. The bank of the Basingstoke Canal seems to be particularly suitable, although surface stones are scarce there.

Colony foundation may be by large groups (20+) of newly fertile queens. Such groups have been found under stones, without workers, within a few hundred metres of large mature colonies. Alates are present in July, but nothing appears to be recorded about their mating behaviour.

M.rubra is probably under-recorded in Surrey because it lives in sites which are not particularly favourable to other ants, and are therefore not attractive to ant recorders. It has been found in similar situations throughout mainland Britain and Ireland.

Myrmica ruginodis Nylander, 1846   PLATES 8, 12, 15

Status in Surrey: Abundant and shade-tolerant

Length: 4-5.5mm

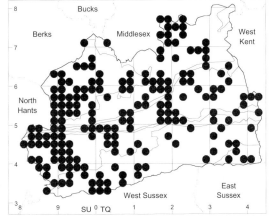

Like *M.rubra*, this ant has antennal scapes which are only slightly curved at the base and have a basal ball-and-socket joint which is on the same axis as the scape. The spines on its propodeum are longer than the space between them, and this space has transverse furrows.

This is one of the commonest and most generally distributed British species. It is shade-tolerant in the south and occurs in nearly all woodland which has dead wood lying on the ground. It usually nests in this dead wood, but it can also nest in tussocks in open wet situations, although other species of *Myrmica* replace it in most open habitats.

The mating behaviour has been observed frequently, since the males accumulate in large numbers over several days on prominent bare areas, including tracks and wooden bridges (and mountain tops in the north). The queens fly in and are promptly grasped by several males. There are occasional reports of these females stinging people after getting under their clothes.

Nest foundation is not well known, but isolated queens can found nests in captivity, although they are too small to rear brood without foraging. Mature nests can have many queens or, commonly, just one queen. Two sizes of queen have been distinguished, but these mate indiscriminately with males across the size range – or possibly with some bias towards the opposite extreme of male size when queens of both sizes occur together on one mating site. These are not, therefore, two separate species.

M.ruginodis has been recorded throughout the British Isles, including the offshore islands.

Myrmica sulcinodis Nylander, 1846   PLATE 15

Status in Surrey: Rare on wet heaths

Length: 4-6mm

This ant is distinctively more bicoloured and rugose than the common *Myrmica* species. The gaster is shiny black and the thorax is dark red in mature workers or yellow in recently hatched individuals. The antennal scapes are more sharply curved than those of the previous species, but the basal ball-and-socket joint is on the same axis as the shaft of the scape.

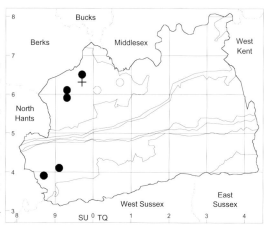

Some observers report that they can hear this species stridulating by moving the gastral segments over one another in the manner of a concertina. All *Myrmica* and most other myrmicines have a ridge-and-file sculpture on the overlap of the dorsal sclerites, but the other species are not reported to be audible without amplification.

This is one of the few ants characteristic of wet heath. It nests in raised lumps or ridges of peat in sparse vegetation, but either moves away or dies out in old tall Ericaceae or dense *Molinia* grass.

M.sulcinodis is very local and rare in Surrey, probably because heaths are not managed for its special requirements, and the plant succession has become too fast through modern-day nitrogen pollution. The most recent records are from Stickledown Rifle Range in 1995, but the other local sites at Chobham and Thursley have become unsuitable. It should still be present somewhere in those districts, so further search may be worthwhile.

There are records of *M.sulcinodis* from boggy heaths scattered locally throughout England and Scotland.

Myrmica scabrinodis Nylander, 1846 PLATES 15, 16

Status in Surrey: Abundant in sunny sites

Length: 4-5mm

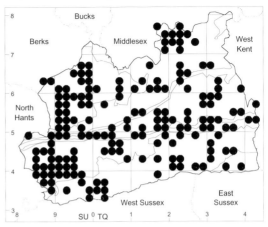

The antennal scapes of this and the following species need careful examination to distinguish them. If an antenna is pulled off and examined under a microscope, the basal ball-and-socket joint will be seen to be displaced from the axis of the shaft by a right-angled bend close to the base. This feature is vital to identifying this and the three following species. In *M.scabrinodis* there is neither a lateral tooth nor a flange along the shaft at the bend. It will only become clear with experience what is meant by these distinctions, but the photographs should help.

M.scabrinodis is a common species in most sunny habitats which are not extremely dry. In wet sites it nests in tussocks, but elsewhere under stones or bare soil. It also frequently shares the mounds of *Lasius flavus* and preys on the other species. J.E.Moxon has described some interesting defensive behaviour in reaction to *L.flavus*. The *M.scabrinodis* bend the gaster forward between the legs, to exude chemicals from the sting, and form ranks side-by-side, with heads forward, across any avenue of access by the enemy. This strategy is successful in artificial observation nests, and is likely to have been evolved to cope specifically with sharing nest-sites with *L.flavus*. This ant has also been observed to actively displace *M.ruginodis* from a favourable nest-site under a stone.

Mating flights take place in July around the tops of isolated tall trees or buildings, and the pairs then fall to the ground. Colony foundation, as far as we know, is by isolated queens foraging in order to rear a few small workers in the year after mating.

This ant is probably present in all rural and suburban areas of Surrey, but is absent from arable farmland unless headlands are left uncultivated. Specimens should be retained in case of confusion with closely similar species which might in future be found in Surrey.

It has been recorded throughout the British Isles, except for the Orkneys and Shetlands.

Myrmica sabuleti Meinert, 1861   PLATES 8, 16

Status in Surrey: Local in dry, sunny sites

Length: 4-5mm

The basal bend of the scape of *M.sabuleti* has a flange extending along the shaft, not transversely around it. This is not easy to see, but, once the scape is placed so as to be seen from above the head, the feature is distinctive.

This species is famous for being the host of the Large Blue Butterfly, but has always been much more widespread and abundant than

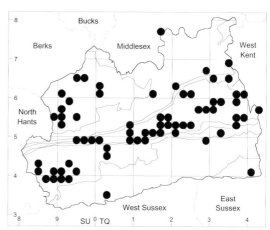

the butterfly. It is typical of the hot dry parts of chalk downs and sandy heaths, where it replaces *M.scabrinodis*. The nests are usually under stones which are undisturbed by large grazers. However, the ants die out in tall herbage so some light-footed grazing by sheep is needed on chalk downs, while, on heathland, the bare patches produced by burning or scraping can be helpful.

This ant differs little in behaviour from *M.scabrinodis*, but *L.flavus* is not usually a coexisting species. It has to interact with *L.alienus* or *L.psammophilus* in the same habitats, and *L.alienus* can displace it.

There is an interesting variety of *M.sabuleti* on Denbies Hillside. It has spatulate hairs instead of the usual filamentous ones, and occurs in the same nests as ordinary individuals. Alates with this feature have not yet been found, so the taxonomic status of this strange "variety" remains uncertain.

The Surrey distribution of *M.sabuleti* is dependent on its special habitat requirements. The ant is usually present where these are suitable, but it is less abundant on heaths than on chalk grassland. There are some records from bare patches on heavy clay soils, although these sites are more usually occupied by *M.scabrinodis*.

The species has been recorded from most of mainland Britain and Ireland.

Myrmica lobicornis Nylander,1846   PLATE 16

Status in Surrey: Local on some heaths, not well recorded

Length: 3.5-4.5mm

In this species, the basal bend of the scape has a sharp tooth projecting from the outside of the angle. It is slightly smaller than other *Myrmica*, and usually has a gaster which is obviously darker than the trunk. It is typically a scarce heathland species in Surrey, but can occur on the margins in hot sites which no longer have any heathland vegetation.

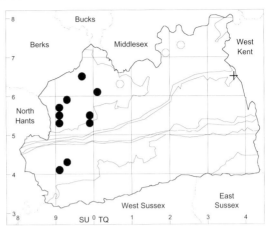

M.lobicornis is probably under-recorded, and has been little studied, It has small nests and very inconspicuous foragers, and may perhaps be overlooked in mistake for *M.scabrinodis*.

The ant is widespread, but sparsely recorded, in open habitats in England and Scotland.

Myrmica schencki Emery, 1895   PLATE 16

Status in Surrey: Local in sunny sites, not well recorded

Length: 4-6mm

In this species, the basal bend of the scape has a large blunt tooth which is accommodated by a larger-than-usual hollow in the head around the antennal base. This hollow is needed to fold the toothed antennae back onto the head and it produces a narrower forehead between the antennae than is seen in other *Myrmica*

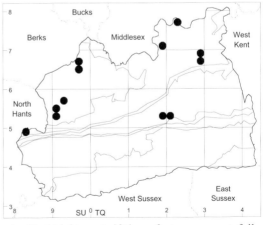

species. *M.schencki* can be confused with *M.lobicornis* if these features are not fully appreciated, but it is a more uniform colour and is similar in size and behaviour to *M.rubra*. The foragers can be found among aphids on tall herbs and shrubs.

Most accounts give its habitat as the hottest dry sites, and it is certainly found in these on chalk downs, but it also occurs, rather unpredictably, in other sunny sites on heaths or in grassland. On Chobham Common there was a nest on the crest of a bomb crater, but this was trodden into extinction by cattle which were intended to be a tool of conservation management!

Abroad, it has been recorded to build a tube upwards around its nest entrance, but this has not been recorded in Surrey.

Mating flights occur around tall buildings, and the pairs then fall to the ground. There are apparently no records of flights in Surrey, but a spectacular flight was recorded, in August, around the flagpole on the highest point of Dover Castle. In spring the queens can be found foraging alone, and presumably also found new nests alone.

M.schencki is usually regarded as a rare species (rated "Notable" in the Red Data Book) and it is certainly infrequently recorded. Our records from Surrey underline this impression of rarity. Several of the records are from the tops of banks in the sun, and these are probably the most likely sites for nests.

There are scattered records from the southern half of England and from Ireland.

Myrmica karavajevi (Arnoldi, 1930)

Status in Surrey: Only one old record in 1953

This is a workerless parasite of *M.scabrinodis* and *M.sabuleti* which was previously called *Sifolinia laurae*. There are only two or three British records, including one from Surrey. Falk, in his review of the Red Data Book species (1991), quotes this as Chobham Common in 1953.

The queen of *M.karavajevi* takes over the nest of its host by some unknown means. Workers of the host continue to be produced, but the only winged sexuals are of the parasite. Queens and males are produced in large numbers and are recognisable by their small size. They are slightly smaller in length than workers of their host. Additionally, the males have only twelve segments in their antennae, rather than thirteen, and the queens have projections from the underside of the waist segments.

Very small alate *Myrmica* should be examined, when found in nests, and any very small isolated queens could also be this species.

Genus *Leptothorax*

These are inconspicuous small ants, often nesting unnoticed within the foraging territory of much larger species. They appear to be chemically "invisible", which has two problems for them. They cannot use scent trails to recruit foragers to a large stationary food source and, secondly, they have little resistance to the mite infestations which can starve captive colonies by repelling the ants from food. The lack of chemical defence by these ants is not known to be a disadvantage in the field, and it is possible that they gain protection from being with larger aggressive species. The genus has sometimes been divided into two, but a single genus is retained here.

Leptothorax acervorum (Fabricius, 1793)   PLATE 9

Status in Surrey: Widely distributed, but not well recorded

Length: 3.5-4mm

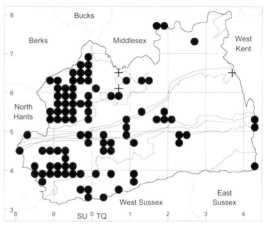

The first impression is of a small slim *Myrmica*, but with distinctive blackish antennal clubs and only eleven segments in the antennae. It is non-aggressive and rapidly escapes into crevices if disturbed.

The nests are usually in dead wood or bark, but sometimes in stone walls or the peaty topsoil of heaths. Full sun is unnecessary, although the nests do not persist in full shade. The ants are able to nest in the margins of nests of *F.sanguinea*, and occasionally in those of *F.rufa*, but are clearly not dependent upon the much larger ants, because they more frequently nest alone.

No records of them tending aphids in the field have been made, although, in captivity, they show the full aphid-tending behaviour to myrmecophilous root aphids. (This is a very easy species to keep and to rear alates.) In the field, they do lick honeydew from leaves, and eat small arthropods. When fed in captivity, after a period of starvation, they stridulate obviously when finding sugar, but this is inaudible without amplification. The recruitment of other workers follows, although proof that this is by communication needs further research.

The species is widespread in Surrey and occasionally abundant in open pine woods with dead sticks on the ground providing nest-sites. Most nests are small with one queen and less than 20 workers, but some nests in stumps or in the bark of standing pines can be much larger, with many queens. The alate queens fly in July and can presumably found nests alone, but need to forage for food.

There are records from the whole of the British Isles with the exception of the Shetlands and a few other smaller islands.

Leptothorax nylanderi (Förster, 1850)

Status in Surrey: Local in old woodland and parkland

Length: 2.5-3.5mm

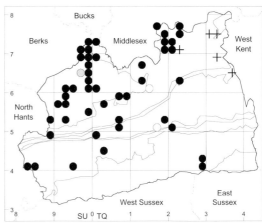

This ant is smaller and paler than *L.acervorum* with a conspicuous dark band on the gaster. Also, the antennae have twelve segments and their clubs are not darkened. It is usually found on the trunks of old oaks in parkland, along with *Lasius brunneus*, but it can occur much more widely in other habitats with woody plants, even occasionally in hedgerows. The nests are frequently in bark crevices, but can also be in other cavities, such as nutshells with a weevil hole for an entrance. There is usually one queen in each small nest, but occasionally several queens can be found in larger nests with over a hundred workers.

The ant is not commonly recorded because of its small size and its tendency to forage along the cracks in bark. It is abundant in Windsor and Richmond Parks and possibly occurs throughout rural Surrey wherever there are old trees.

It has been recorded from the southern half of England and from Wales.

Formicoxenus nitidulus (Nylander, 1846)　PLATE 6

Status in Surrey: Occurs wherever *F.rufa* is well established

Length: 2.8-3mm

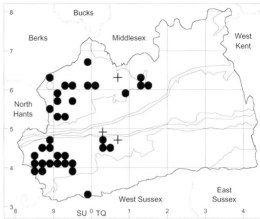

This species is always an inquiline in nests of the Wood Ant, and is present in all areas where the host is well established. *F.nitidulus* is tiny, shiny, and brown with a black gaster. The males are wingless and worker-like, except for their longer, curved antennae.

Its nests are inside tough bark, sticks or dead bracken stems, deep in the Wood Ant mounds, and can be found by pushing in old bracken stems and pulling them out several months later. A less destructive method of recording the inquiline is to look for males on the surface of the mounds. They appear from August to October and can most often be seen when the Wood Ants are less active, either early in the morning or, in declining autumn temperatures, during the day.

Several nests of *F.nitidulus* often occur in one host mound and this gets over the problem of inbreeding, of the wingless males mating with their sisters. This mating takes place on the surface of the mound and can be observed early in the morning. The fertilised queens fly off to found nests with other hosts, or perhaps return to the same mound. Some individuals have been found that are intermediate in anatomy between workers and queens, but they probably do not lay fertilised eggs and, if so, could only produce sons.

It is very difficult to observe this species in captive nests, because of its aggressive hosts, and we therefore rely on guesswork for understanding much of its biology. When without nest material, the host hunts the *F.nitidulus*, grasps it with its mandibles, and squirts it with acid. The inquiline survives this at first, but cannot settle to normal behaviour and eventually dies. When with nest material, the ants cannot be observed because they keep under cover. Perhaps infra-red illumination without nest material could work, since Wood Ants are visual predators; they would, however, still be attracted to the infra-red source for warmth.

This species may be found wherever the Wood Ant is well established, and similarly in the nests of its northern relatives, *F.lugubris* and the Scottish *F.aquilonia*.

Stenamma debile (Förster, 1850) and *S.westwoodi* Westwood, 1839   PLATE 9

Status in Surrey: Shade-tolerant and inadequately recorded

Length: 3.5-4mm

There is an awkward taxonomic problem with this genus. All early North European records were determined as *S.westwoodi*, but a revision of the genus by Dubois in 1993 assigned all available specimens to *S.debile*, except some from Western Europe including the British Isles. The differences are small, and specimens of both species, for comparison, are needed to be confident of identification. The clearest difference, in females,

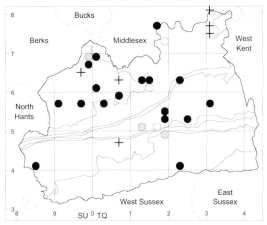

Distribution of S.debile

is a much narrower central area between the antennal bases of *S.westwoodi*. In Surrey, there are few records of this species: one nest in a hollow flint in chalk woodland on top of Denbies Hillside, a worker from Colekitchen Down, and an alate from a nearby site. However, *S.debile* is more widespread.

Stenamma is a subterranean ant like a small *Myrmica*, but much slimmer. The slim waist and the eyes, reduced to very few facets, are diagnostic of the genus in Britain. Both species occupy small nests under large, deeply embedded stones or inside hollow flints, but can use other buried cavities. A nest of *S.debile* from Wentworth Great Wood was in a discarded metal toothpaste tube and was exceptionally large, with eleven queens and about fifty workers. One queen and a dozen workers are more normal numbers.

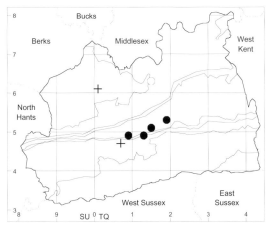

Distribution of S.westwoodi

Records are more often made by entomologists extracting samples of leaf litter using Tullgren funnels or similar apparatus, and this may indicate the usual foraging behaviour. In captivity the ants recoil from myrmecophilous aphids or even kill them. They sometimes accept small dead arthropods as food, but in these conditions their behaviour is abnormal, for they also eat any of their own pupae that may be present.

The nests are normally in old woodland in total shade, but they can persist in secluded gardens which have a woodland history. The species are grossly under-recorded throughout their range, mainly because foragers are not seen without using methods which are unusual for myrmecology. The habitat is also a poor one for ant collecting.

Mating flights occur late in the year, usually in September, and the ants may then be captured in moth traps or Malaise traps.

Stenamma are recorded from the southern half of England, Wales and Ireland. The Irish specimens have been identified as *S.westwoodi*, but many of the English ones are *S.debile*. However, the taxonomic difficulty and rareness of collection make further distribution detail uncertain.

Myrmecina graminicola (Latreille, 1802)   PLATE 9

Status in Surrey: Local in hot sites on clay

Length: 3-3.5mm

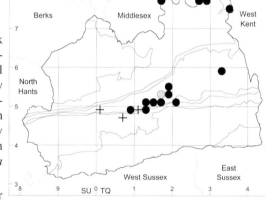

This is a distinctive small black myrmicine which, after disturbance, remains still for several seconds before moving slowly away. It may curl up like a pill-woodlouse when still. It nests in those hottest sites which do not dry out easily – often in clay patches on chalk downs, along with *Ponera coarctata*.

The nests are usually under embedded stones, or in hollow flints, and have one queen and up to thirty workers. Much larger nests have been recorded, with multiple queens, but these must be rare.

The ant is most easily detected by placing baits of minced meat under stones, away from larger species. In captivity it will eat dead arthropods and sweet substances, and is a particularly easy species to keep and to rear alates.

Mating flights occur in August and September. After mating, the isolated queens are able to rear workers in captivity, if fed.

As expected, the Surrey records are almost confined to the chalk and adjacent clays, but it might possibly be found elsewhere, if searched for. The records from south London probably result from the temperature being a few degrees higher in this major built-up area.

There are records from Britain as far north as the Wash.

Tetramorium caespitum (Linnaeus, 1758)   PLATES 9, 11

Status in Surrey: Local in hot
   sites on dry heath

Length: 2.5-3.5mm

This small black myrmicine is an
aggressive, actively stinging, large-
nested species. The alates are very
much larger than the workers, and
this feature is unique among ants
on Surrey heaths. It is confined
to hot sites, under stones or in
bare patches, and is an excellent
indicator of dry heath. Fires are
easily survived.

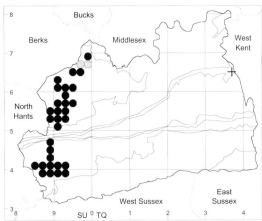

It is unique in Britain for storing
seeds and feeding its larvae directly with them. The seeds of grasses, heather and birch
are the commonest ones found in the nests. Both prey and honeydew are also eaten, but
foraging up plants is very rarely reported.

Flights occur in July and, in the morning, alates may be found trapped in puddles – this
suggests that they fly at night. If this is true, records from moth traps can be expected.
Queens are occasionally found alone on the surface, and can certainly start new nests
alone without needing to forage for food.

There are records from all the major dry heaths in Surrey. The ant is vulnerable to lack
of management, since continuous dense tall heather is unsuitable for a species that does
little mound-building and needs bare ground. Chobham Common is in danger of losing
it, and Horsell Common has too few dry sites. On most of the heaths it relies on summer
fires for suitable ground.

The British distribution corresponds to hot sites in southern England, north and south
Wales, southern Ireland and some Scottish coasts. In coastal areas the habitat is frequently
close-cropped grassland with stones on the surface.

Anergates atratulus (Schenck, 1852)   PLATE 9

Status in Surrey: Very rare, only where *Tetramorium* is abundant

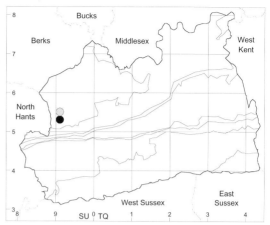

This is a workerless parasite of *Tetramorium*. The queens are, initially, no bigger than workers of the host, while the males are pupoid and wingless. These males only appear in small numbers and spend most of their time mating, while lying in a wide shallow groove down the back of the queen's gaster. The queens are produced in large numbers and, once fertilised, fly off on any fine day. They enter those *Tetramorium* nests which have no queens of their own. Several *Anergates* queens may be accepted, thus avoiding the problem of inbreeding through the wingless males only mating with their sisters. The queens become exceptionally physogastric so their initial small size is less of a disadvantage.

This species must require large populations of *Tetramorium* for continued success, so it is not surprising that the only Surrey records were from Tunnel Hill in 1974 and from Ash Ranges in April 1996 (larvae only). It has not been recorded again, despite many searches of the military lands, but it could still be there. *Tetramorium* nests with *Tetramorium* brood (the large alate pupae are especially obvious) do not have *Anergates*, and this helps the search without needing to badly damage the host nests. Under a magnifying glass, the *Anergates* larvae are obviously more hairy and are also not barrel-shaped like the larvae of *Tetramorium* workers, but have the body slightly narrowed into a waist. Small alate pupae are obviously not *Tetramorium*.

Anergates has also been recorded from Dungeness, the New Forest and south Devon, but it is doubtful if anywhere else in Britain has an adequate population of *Tetramorium* to support it.

Subfamily Dolichoderinae

These ants have a single segment in the waist (very small and difficult to see in *Tapinoma*) and a transverse slit for a terminal orifice with no sting. They produce a distinctive repellent smell and the pupae have no cocoons. The males and queens are of similar size. This is a large subfamily overseas, but only one genus is present in Britain.

Tapinoma erraticum (Latreille, 1798) (and *T.ambiguum* Emery, 1925) PLATE 10

Status in Surrey: Rare in hot sites on dry heath

Length: 2.5-4mm

These are fast-running, small black ants with a very mobile gaster which is pointed upward when the ant is disturbed. This posture is accompanied by a chemical discharge from the terminal aperture, which has a similar effect on its enemies to that produced by a skunk. Even the large *Formica sanguinea* can be repelled by it.

There are two very similar species, only clearly distinguishable by the male genitalia, but also dubiously by a small difference in the shape of the clypeal notch of workers and queens. This notch is as deep as it is wide in *T.erraticum*, but shallower than wide in *T.ambiguum*. Both species have been recorded from Britain, but, in Surrey, males have been examined only from Thursley Common. These and the females are *T.erraticum*, and it would be valuable to examine more specimens from any site in case we have *T.ambiguum* as well. The alates are produced in June.

Small nest-mounds of coarse debris are made in hot sites on heaths, and these nests are vulnerable to trampling. They are usually formed around a small plant on a bare area, or in a particularly hot metal object such as an empty can or cartridge. A population of *Tapinoma* on Shrike Hill,Thursley Common, was monitored after a fire in 1976. The first nest was found in 1981, then seven nests were found in 1982 and the number rose to a maximum of 14 in 1985, presumably because it takes several years for new foundresses to produce large enough nests to be discovered. Most of the nests were in food cans discarded by military trainees, which provided hot spots for ideal growth. Alates were produced by some nests in 1986, but from then on the numbers declined until there was only one nest found in 1991. No nests were found after 1994 when the heather canopy had almost entirely closed and the cans were rusted into collapsed debris.

Little is known about the natural longevity of ant nests, but in this case ten years is a very rough minimum estimate. It might be longer if plant succession was slower, but, following a more recent fire nearby, the vegetation has recovered to a similar degree in ten years instead of fifteen.

Fires are likely to be beneficial, if well-timed. However, they are likely to be more dangerous to these shallow-nested species than to the other ants of dry heathland, and *Tapinoma* is much rarer now. The last record from Chobham Common was in 1966, and very few nests persist on the military lands or on Thursley Common. There are no other modern records from Surrey.

All British records of *Tapinoma* are from southern England, and it can also occur on coastal sites which are not heaths.

Subfamily Ponerinae

This subfamily is supposedly primitive, but it includes a wide range of specialised species, although only one species is a British native. The ants have one large segment in the waist and also a constriction between the first two segments of the gaster. Stings are present and the pupae have cocoons.

Ponera coarctata (Latreille, 1802)   PLATES 10, 16

Status in Surrey: Local in hot sites on clay, under-recorded

Length: 3mm

This is a tiny dark brown ant which retreats rapidly into very narrow crevices when disturbed. When first seen, this behaviour and its slim build will remind the observer of a small staphylinid (rove beetle). It is restricted to hot habitats which do not dry out, so most of the records are from clay on chalk downs, often together with *Myrmecina*. It is similarly

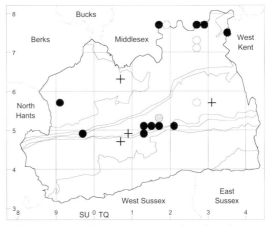

recorded from south London where the average ambient temperature is a few degrees higher than in rural districts.

The "nests" are very small and consist of tunnels ramifying through the soil. Larger ants are avoided by living in tunnels which are too narrow for them. Single queens are usual, and alates are produced in August. They can be found, in hot weather, alighting on bare sites (including parked cars!). Baits of minced meat attract workers and also isolated queens, so, presumably, nests are founded alone. Another successful method of collection is to sieve moss from suitable habitats.

Care is needed when recording because, in warm sites, there may be an introduced species, *Hypoponera punctatissima*, which is usually confined to hot-houses. It will certainly be mistaken for *P.coarctata* unless a careful high-power examination is undertaken. *H.punctatissima* does not have the small ventral tooth on the petiole, and its males are worker-like.

This ant is listed as "Notable" in the Red Data Book, but is under-recorded. British records are all south of a line from Hertfordshire to south Wales.

Other species

A number of species have been recorded from southern England but not yet found in Surrey.

Lasius sabularum (Bondroit, 1918)
Extremely similar to *L.mixtus*, but the males have teeth along the mandibular biting edge as in *L.umbratus* – rather than smooth with only apical teeth as in *L.mixtus*. Male specimens are needed before it can confidently be recorded. (See Seifert, 1988.)

Formica pratensis Retzius, 1783
A very darkly marked, hairy, wood ant previously recorded from heaths in Hampshire, the Isle of Wight and Dorset, but now apparently extinct in Britain.

Formica exsecta Nylander, 1846
The specimen in the Oxford University Museum labelled "*Formica sanguinea* without emarginate clypeus, Woking, May 24th, 1913", has the very concave rear head margin characteristic of *F.exsecta*. Only Horsell Common in that district remains in adequate condition and no *F.exsecta* has been recorded since. It is a rare heath species which would be a valuable, but unlikely, discovery now.

Formica lemani Bondroit, 1917
Similar to *F.fusca*, but with thoracic hairs; widespread in the north and on moorland further south.

Strongylognathus testaceus (Schenck, 1852)
Parasitic on *Tetramorium*. Has sickle-shaped mandibles which indicate it was a slave maker, but it has ceased to make raids. The nearest record is from the New Forest – otherwise a Dorset speciality.

Solenopsis fugax (Latreille, 1798)
A tiny, pale brown, usually coastal ant with very populous nests in dense clay or in rock clefts. Is able to raid the brood of larger ants via escape tunnels too small for the defenders to pursue. Usually found where cliff falls are frequent enough to provide bare habitat, but infrequently enough to give time for development of large nests. Nearest records are from Dorset and it is unlikely to be recorded in Surrey.

Leptothorax albipennis (Curtis, 1854)

Similar to *L.nylanderi*, but with dark antennal clubs. Usually coastal, nesting under rock flakes or in similar cavities. Unlikely to be in Surrey.

Leptothorax interruptus (Schenck, 1852)

Similar again, but on dry heathland, nesting in peaty topsoil or dead plant bases. Nearest recent records from Dungeness and the New Forest.

Myrmica specioides Bondroit, 1918

Similar to *M.scabrinodis*, but conspicuously more aggressive and recorded in Britain only from hot and dry coastal sandy sites. *M.scabrinodis* has been mistakenly recorded as this species, but the petiole of *M.speciodes* has a rounded rear face and not the taller flat top of that of *M.scabrinodis.*

Myrmica hirsuta Elmes, 1978

A rare very hairy parasite of *M.sabuleti.* Workers are scarce and the numerous alates are clearly smaller than alates of its host (which are not produced when the parasite is present).

Myrmica vandeli Bondroit, 1920

This species has been added to the British list very recently. Workers are very similar to *M.scabrinodis*, but the males have long antennal scapes like those of *M.sabuleti* (see Elmes et al, 2001). Any record of the common *M.scabrinodis* might possibly refer to this species and any males and alate queens collected should be kept with workers from the same nest. Workers of *M.vandeli* can possibly be separated by having a shallow concavity in the anterior border to the clypeus and greater hairiness than *M.scabrinodis*, which has a smooth round slightly convex clypeal margin and hairiness similar to other *Myrmica.* Warm moist habitats appear to be needed.

Some introduced species occurring in heated buildings, or in other artificially hot sites, have been recorded from Surrey. They are much rarer now that effective insecticides are used. A very small and inconspicuous myrmicine, Pharaoh's Ant, *Monomorium pharaonis*, was once widespread in hospitals and bakeries but has effectively been eliminated by baits charged with a hormone that distorts its larval development. *Plagiolepis pygmaea* (Formicinae) is still common in greenhouses growing tropical plants, and is so small that the workers are invisible unless close examination of its foraging area is made. Species of *Tapinoma*, similar to our native ones, are also still occasionally found, but the Kew glasshouses, where many species were recorded by Donisthorpe, are no longer a rich collecting ground.

WHAT OF THE FUTURE?

One of the main values of an atlas is to form a basis for assessing changes of distribution in the future. It would be wrong to assume that this atlas was a complete record of the distribution of all species found in Surrey at the beginning of the 21st century, but some changes will certainly become obvious within a few decades of its publication. These will become more interesting and perhaps more serious with the passage of time. Both increases and decreases are possible, and should be monitored wherever practicable.

The gains are more interesting and worth discussing first. The much publicised climate warming has already been accompanied by big increases in the abundance and range of actively flying insects, for example the Bee-wolf, *Philanthus triangulum* (a solitary wasp). No ant species has yet been claimed to show a similar increase, but *Solenopsis fugax*, *Myrmica specioides*, *Tapinoma* spp. and *Formica cunicularia* are all potentially capable of colonising sites further north, while *Tetramorium* may become a widespread pavement ant as it is in much of Europe. *Myrmica rugulosa*, *Crematogaster scutellaris* and *Lasius emarginatus* are possible examples of many potential invaders from nearby on the continent. Not all possible invaders are welcome. For example, the Argentine Ant, *Linepithema humile*, displaces other species because it does not form separate nests and fights with other ants, but not with its own species. The resulting losses to ants and other insects can be devastating, so its introduction must be avoided. *Lasius neglectus* (synonymised with *L.turcicus* by Seifert on morphological grounds) is also a danger for this reason.

Neither should any other species be released outside its natural range, because the results are unpredictable and ants can be particularly dominating ecologically.

On the other hand, the species of *Formica* seem to be particularly vulnerable to extinction, and *F.pratensis* has already become extinct in Britain. It is unlikely to fly across the Channel from France, so its recolonisation is less likely than invasion by some of the new species mentioned above. *F.rufibarbis* is also nearly extinct in mainland Britain, but there is perhaps a greater probability of this species recolonising if our climate warms by several degrees, as predicted.

Local extinctions are certain for many of our species because man's activities have a much greater negative impact on habitats than any positive impact on ants from climate warming. Our heathland species, such as *Tapinoma*, are probably the ones most at risk from habitat loss. If one compares a series of sites, such as Clapham Common, Hampstead Heath, Wimbledon Common, Chobham Common and the Rifle Ranges, it is evident that recreational impact near large human populations is progressively fatal to natural history. The possibility of controlling access and use has not been faced by conservationists, and most other people do not think that their pleasure could be less important than that of future generations. Even if access is limited to naturalists, they can become so numerous that they destroy that which they come to see. Certainly designating an area as a "Park" ("National" or otherwise) is an invitation to use it primarily for recreation. The Rifle Ranges are the best site for ants because, firstly, they are protected from visitors and, secondly, hot summer fires have been frequent enough to keep pioneer heath available. This can be underlined by counting the species present at different sites, omitting the woodland areas within their boundaries. Chobham has 17 species definitely persisting into the 21st century, with two more recorded in the 1990's (*M.schencki* and *M.sulcinodis*). Only one species still present at Chobham has not been recorded from the Ranges – *F.cunicularia*. On the other hand, the Ranges also have records of *F.picea* and *Anergates* which have not been recorded from anywhere else in Surrey, and *Tapinoma* is still present there, although not recorded from Chobham for forty years. *Tetramorium* is now very scarce at Chobham, but widely distributed on the Ranges – hopefully numerous enough there to support *Anergates* still.

Unfortunately, nature reserves are frequently mismanaged for soil-living animals, and more thought about the aims of a particular management strategy is necessary. Grazing by large herbivores may be valuable for some things, but can eliminate soil-living insects by trampling them. Trials, with experimentally designed controls, are needed to decide which species are favoured or killed. It is also never a good idea to subject the whole of a site to a new management regime.

At the very least, one might expect *L.niger, L.flavus, L.brunneus, F.fusca, M.ruginodis, M.scabrinodis* and *L.nylanderi* to persist, with gardens and parks as the remaining preserved habitats, but this is surely a dismal future!

APPENDIX 1 – Some sites for
ants of special interest

A summary of important records after 1990 of species that are specialists in these habitat types. Asterisks indicate nationally rare species which are realistically recorded in less than 12 Surrey tetrads.

In the tables below, the figures indicate numbers of species present, with asterisks representing how many of these are national rarities; e.g. under Heathlands / The Greensand commons / Thursley, 8** means there are eight species, of which two are national rarities.

---

1. HEATHLANDS, where the species included are: *Lasius psammophilus, L.meridionalis, Formica rufibarbis*, F.cunicularia, F.picea*, Myrmica sabuleti, M.sulcinodis*, M.lobicornis, Tetramorium caespitum, Anergates atratulus** and *Tapinoma erraticum**.

The Greensand commons			The Bagshot Sand heathlands		
Thursley	8**	SU 9040+	**Ash Ranges**	9***	SU89+50+
Hankley	5	SU 8840+	**Pirbright Ranges**		
Frensham	6*	SU 84+40+	**(incl Colony Bog)**	10****	SU91+57+
Witley	3	SU 92+39+	**Brentmoor**	4	SU93+60+
Crooksbury	2	SU 88+45+	**Lightwater C'try Park**	4	SU90+61+
Blackheath	4	TQ 02+45+	**Chobham**	10***	SU95+63+
			Whitmoor	3	SU98+53
			Horsell	4	SU98+60
			Oxshott	3	TQ1461

---

2. CHALK DOWNLAND with numbers of specialist species:
Lasius alienus, Formica cunicularia, Myrmica sabuleti, Myrmecina graminicola* and *Ponera coarctata**.

Denbies Hillside	5**	TQ13+50	**Hackhurst**	3	TQ09+48+
Box Hill	5**	TQ17+51+	**Colekitchen reserve**	2*	TQ0848+
Dawcombe	3	TQ2152	**Pewley Down**	1	TQ0048
Riddlesdown	3*	TQ32+59+	**Hog's Back**	3*	SU9648
Colley Hill	3	TQ2452			

---

3. PARKS WITH OLD TREES: *Lasius brunneus* and *Leptothorax nylanderi* are present in each one.

Richmond	TQ18++70++
Windsor	SU9769
Farnham	SU83+47+

APPENDIX 2 – Glossary

alate – a winged ant (or aphid).

carton – chewed wood (sometimes with soil), as material for nest partitions.

clypeus – the upper lip of insects.

clypeal notch – a concavity in the centre of the anterior margin of the upper lip.

cornicle – a paired tubular appendage projecting from the rear dorsal surface of aphids.

emarginate – a concave margin.

formic acid – H-COOH.

frass – (here) fine debris produced by insects biting off particles of wood.

frontal triangle – a triangular area immediately posterior to the clypeus.

funiculus – the segmented distal half of an elbowed antenna.

gaster – the rounded body region posterior to the waist.

inquiline – a species living in a nest made by another species.

Malaise trap – a fixed trap for catching flying insects.

myrmecophile – a species normally closely associated with ants.

petiole – the segment forming part of the waist.

physogastric – with a gaster distended by a large number of eggs.

pilosity – the distribution of "hairs" on an insect's surface.

pooter – a collecting device for picking up small insects by oral suction.

post-petiole – a second waist segment in myrmicines.

propodeum – the rearmost section of the trunk anterior to the waist.

prothorax – the anterior part of the trunk.

pupoid – shaped like a pupa.

RDB – the English Nature rating of rarity of species in a "Red Data Book".

rugose – wrinkled surface of the cuticle.

scape – the long first segment of an antenna, attached directly to the head.

sclerite – a hard section of exoskeleton.

spatulate hairs – unusually flattened hairs with a blade-like shape.

stridulation – chirping noises produced by rubbing a cuticle ridge on a file.

thorax – the section of the body behind the head.

tibia – the middle long section of leg between femur (thigh) and foot.

transect – an ecologist's term for a marked series of study locations.

trophallaxis – regurgitation to feed another individual.

trunk – the thorax plus the propodeum which is one abdominal segment.

Tullgren funnel – a method for extracting active insects from soil by heat and drying.

APPENDIX 3 – Bibliography

Some of the literature listed here contains information quoted in the previous pages, but most is intended to give additional information or even, in a few cases, the opposing side of controversial points.

IDENTIFICATION: KEYS AND NOMENCLATURE OF BRITISH ANTS

Collingwood, C.A., 1979.
The Formicidae (Hymenoptera) of Fennoscandia and Denmark. Fauna Entomologica Scandinavica **8**. Scandinavian Science Press, Klampenborg, Denmark.

Czechowski, W., Radchenko, A. and Czechowska, W., 2002.
The Ants (Hymenoptera, Formicidae) of Poland. Museum and Institute of Zoology, Warszawa.

Skinner, G.J. and Allen, G.W., 1996.
Ants. Naturalists' Handbooks 24. Richmond Publishing Co., Slough.

Sweeney, R.C.H., 1950.
Identification of British ants (Hym., Formicidae) with keys to the genera and species. *Entomologists' Gazette* **1**: 64-83.

MONOGRAPHS ON SEPARATE GROUPS

Dubois, M.B., 1993.
What's in a name? A clarification of *Stenamma westwoodi, S.debile*, and *S.lippulum. Sociobiology* **21**: 299-334.

Elmes, G.W., 1978.
A morphometric comparison of the closely related species of *Myrmica* (Formicidae) including a new species from England. *Systematic Entomology* **3**: 131-145.

Elmes, G.W., Radchenko, A.G. and Thomas, J.A., 2003.
First records of *Myrmica vandeli* Bondroit (Hymenoptera, Formicidae) for Britain. *Br. J. Ent. Nat. Hist.* **16**: 145-152.

Seifert, B., 1988.
A Revision of the European Species of the Ant Subgenus *Chthonolasius* (Insecta, Hymenoptera, Formicidae). *Ent. Abh. Staatliches Museum für Tierkunde Dresden* **51**: 140-80.

Seifert, B., 1992.
A taxonomic revision of the Palaearctic Members of the Ant Subgenus *Lasius* s. str. (Hymenoptera: Formicidae). *Abh. Ber. Naturkundemus. Görlitz* **66**: 5-67.

Wardlaw, J.C., Elmes, G.W. and Thomas, J.A., 1998.
Techniques for studying *Maculinea* butterflies: II. Identification guide to *Myrmica* ants found on *Maculinea* sites in Europe. *Journal of Insect Conservation* **2**: 119-127.

Yarrow, I.H.H., 1954
The British ants allied to *Formica fusca* L. (Hym., Formicidae). *Trans. for the Society for British Entomology* **11**: 229-244.

Yarrow, I.H.H., 1955.
The British ants allied to *Formica rufa* L. (Hym., Formicidae). *Trans. for the Society for British Entomology* **12**: 1-48.

RECORDING AND DISTRIBUTION OF BRITISH ANTS

Baroni Urbani, C. and Collingwood, C.A., 1976.
A Numerical Analysis of the Distribution of British Formicidae (Hymenoptera, Aculeata). *Verhandl. Naturf. Ges. Basel* **85**: 51-911.

Barrett, K.E.J., 1963.
Ants (Hym., Formicidae) of the the Chobham Common area of Surrey. *Entomologist's Record and Journal of Variation* **75**: 29-30.

Barrett, K.E.J., 1964.
Formica sanguinea Latreille (Hym., Formicidae) in Southern England. *Entomologist's Record and Journal of Variation* **76**: 107-114.

Barrett, K.E.J., 1968.
A survey of the distribution and present status of the Wood Ant, *Formica rufa* L. (Hym., Formicidae), in England and Wales. *Trans. for the Society for British Entomology* **17**: 217-233.

Barrett, K.E.J., 1968.
The distribution of ants in Central Southern England. *Trans. for the Society for British Entomology* **17**: 235-250.

Barrett, K.E.J., 1979.
Provisional Atlas of the Insects of the British Isles, Part 5, Hymenoptera: Formicidae, Ants. Biological Records Centre, Institute of Terrestrial Ecology, Monks Wood Experimental Station, Huntingdon.

Barrett, K.E.J. and Felton, J.C., 1965.
The distribution of the Wood Ant, *Formica rufa* Linnaeus (Hymenoptera, Formicidae), in South-East England. *The Entomologist* **98**: 181-191.

Falk, S., 1991.
A review of the scarce and threatened bees, wasps and ants of Great Britain. *Research and Survey in Nature Conservation No 35*. The Nature Conservancy Council.

Osborne, P.J., 1972.
Insect faunas of Late Devensian and Flandrian age from Church Stretton, Shropshire. *Phil. Trans. of the Royal Society of London* **263**: 327-367.

Pontin, A.J., 1962.
Notes on the collection of British ants in the Hope Department at Oxford. *Entomologists' Mon. Mag.* **98**: 63.

Spooner, G.M., 1968.
Records of three uncommon *Formica* species (Hym., Formicidae). *Entomologists' Mon. Mag.* **104**: 130-131.

GENERAL BIOLOGY OF ANTS

Donisthorpe, H.StJ.K., 1927.
British ants, their life-history and classification. 2nd Ed. Routledge, London.

Hölldobler, B. and Wilson, E.O., 1990.
The Ants. Springer-Verlag, Berlin.

Hölldobler, B. and Wilson, E.O., 1994.
Journey to the Ants. Belknap Press, Cambridge, Mass.

ECOLOGY AND BEHAVIOUR

Brian, M.V., 1952.
Interaction between ant colonies at an artificial nest site.
Entomologists' Mon. Mag. **88**: 84-88.

Brian, M.V., 1964.
Ant distribution in a southern English heath. *J. Anim. Ecol.*
33: 451-461.

Elmes, G.W., 1978.
Populations of *Myrmica* (Formicidae) living on different
types of *Calluna* moorland – a semi-natural habitat of
southern England. *Memorab. Zool* **29**: 41-60.

Giles, J., 2005.
Nitrogen study fertilizes fears of pollution. *Nature* **433**: 791.

King, T.J., 1977.
The plant ecology of ant-hills in calcareous grasslands, parts
I, II and III. *J. Ecol.* 235-315.

King, T.J., 1981.
Ant-hills and grassland history. *J. of Biogeography* 329-334.

Odum, E.P. and Pontin, A.J., 1961.
Population density of the underground ant, *Lasius flavus,* as
determined by tagging with P-32. *Ecology* **42**: 186-8.

Pontin, A.J., 1960.
Field experiments on colony foundation by *Lasius niger* (L.)
and *L.flavus* (F.) (Hym., Formicidae). *Insectes Sociaux*
7: 227-30.

Pontin, A.J., 1961.
The prey of *Lasius niger* (L.) and *L.flavus* (F.) (Hym.,
Formicidae). *Entomologists' Mon. Mag.* **97**: 135-137.

Pontin, A.J., 1961.
A note on the behaviour of *Lasius fuliginosus* (Hym.,
Formicidae). *Entomologists' Mon. Mag.* **97**: 137.

Pontin, A.J., 1961.
Population stabilization and competition between the ants
Lasius flavus (F.) and *L.niger* (L.). *J. of Animal Ecology*
30: 47-54.

Pontin, A.J., 1962.
A method for quick comparison of the total solar radiation incident on different microhabitats. *Ecology* **43**: 740-741.

Pontin, A.J., 1963.
Further considerations of competition and the ecology of the ants *Lasius flavus* (F.) and *L.niger* (L.). *J. of Animal Ecology* **32**: 565-574.

Pontin, A.J., 1969.
Experimental transplantation of nest-mounds of the ant *Lasius flavus* (F.) in a habitat containing also *L.niger* (L.) and *Myrmica scabrinodis* Nyl. *J. of Animal Ecology* **38**: 747-754.

Pontin, A.J., 1976.
Anergates atratulus (Schenck) in Surrey. *Entomologists' Mon. Mag.* **111**: 187.

Pontin, A.J., 1986.
Mating behaviour of *Myrmica schencki* Emery (Hym., Formicidae) *Entomologists' Mon. Mag.* **122**: 176.

Pontin, A.J., 1987.
Nest foundation by large groups of queen ants (Hym., Formicidae). *Entomologists' Mon. Mag.* **123**: 238.

Pontin, A.J., 1990.
Intranest copulation in *Formica rufa* L. (Hym., Formicidae). *Entomologists' Mon. Mag.* **126**: 86.

Pontin, A.J., 1996.
Longevity of ant queens in laboratory nests. *Entomologists' Mon. Mag.* **132**: 184.

Pontin, A.J., 1996.
British *Formica rufibarbis* F. (Hym., Formicidae) is not a hopeless case yet. *Entomologists' Mon. Mag.* **132**: 290.

Pontin, A.J., 1996.
Ant nests, sun and shade – their measurement and significance for invertebrate conservation. *British Wildlife* **8**: 21-27.

Pontin, A.J., 2002.
Notes on the behaviour of *Formicoxenus nitidulus* (Nylander) (Hym., Formicidae). *Entomologists' Mon. Mag.* **138**: 208.

Pontin, A.J., 2004.
Mating behaviour of *Formica rufibarbis* F. (Hym., Formicidae). *Entomologists' Mon. Mag.* **140**: 111.

Pontin, A.J., 2004.
Some notes on *Lasius* (Hym., Formicidae) queens and colony foundation. *Entomologists' Mon. Mag.* **140**: 36.

Prescott, H.W., 1968.
Longevity of *Lasius flavus* F. (Hym., Formicidae). *Entomologists' Mon. Mag.* **104**: 284.

Schlick-Steiner, B.C., Steiner, F.M., and Moder, K., 2003.
Ant nests in linear habitats; a new technique for estimating the density of sedentary organisms. Simulation and case study. *Sociobiology* **42**: 163-174.

Waloff, N., 1957.
The effect of number of queens of the ant *Lasius flavus* (Fabricius) (Hym., Formicidae) on their survival and on the rate of development of the first brood. *Insectes Sociaux* **4**: 392-408.

Waloff, N. and Blackith, R.E., 1962.
The growth and distribution of mounds of *Lasius flavus* (Fabricius) (Hym., Formicidae) in Silwood Park, Berkshire. *J. Animal Ecology* **31**: 421-437.

Woodell, S.E.J., 1974.
Anthill Vegetation in a Norfolk Saltmarsh. *Oecologia (Berl.)* **16**: 221-225.

MYRMECOPHILY

Donisthorpe, H.StJ.K., 1927.
The guests of British ants, their habits and life-histories. Routledge, London.

Elmes, G.W, and Thomas, J.A., 1992.
Complexity of species conservation in managed habitats: interaction between *Maculinea* butterflies and their ant hosts. *Biodiversity Conservation* **1**: 155-169.

Elmes, G.W., Thomas, J.A., Wardlaw, J.C., Hochberg, M., Clarke, R.T. and Simcox, D.J., 1988.
The ecology of *Myrmica* ants in relation to the conservation of *Maculinea* butterflies. *J. Insect Conservation* **2**: 67-78.

Pontin, A.J., 1958.
A preliminary note on the eating of aphids by ants of the genus *Lasius* (Hym., Formicidae). *Entomologists' Mon. Mag.* **94**: 9-11.

Pontin, A.J., 1959.
Some records of predators and parasites adapted to attack aphids attended by ants. *Entomologists' Mon. Mag.* **95**: 154-155.

Pontin, A.J., 1961.
Observations on the keeping of aphid eggs by ants of the genus *Lasius* (Hym., Formicidae). *Entomologists' Mon. Mag.* **96**: 198-199.

Pontin, A.J., 1978.
The numbers and distribution of subterranean aphids and their exploitation by the ant *Lasius flavus* Fabricius. *Ecological Entomology* **3**: 203-207.

Pontin, A.J., 1983.
Aphid eggs and ants of genus *Lasius*. *Entomologists' Mon. Mag.* **119**: 206.

Pontin, A.J., 1989.
Adaptation of aphid eggs to specific ant hosts. *Entomologists' Mon. Mag.* **124**: 4.

Pontin. A.J., 1990.
Plebejus argus L. (Lep., Lycaenidae) pupae in nests of *Lasius niger* (L.) (Hym., Formicidae). Entomologists' Mon. Mag. **126**: 73.

Pontin, A.J., 1990.
Low specificity of Plebejus argus (L.) (Lep., Lycaenidae) to species of *Lasius* (Hym., Formicidae). *Entomologists' Mon. Mag.* **126**: 196.

Way, M.J., 1985.
Mutualism between ants and honeydew producing Homoptera. *Ann. Rev. of Entomology* **8**: 307-344.

INDEX
Figures in bold indicate plate numbers

ANTS

OTHER INVERTEBRATES

THE SURREY WILDLIFE ATLAS SERIES
published by Surrey Wildlife Trust

*"An outstanding monument . . . I am delighted to have them
on my shelves."* – Sir David Attenborough

Butterflies of Surrey by Graham A. Collins
*". . . a delightful book and the best county faunal work on butterflies that
I have read."* – ENTOMOLOGIST'S GAZETTE

Dragonflies of Surrey by Peter Follett
"Well produced, well written . . . at a sensible price." – ENTOMOLOGIST'S RECORD

Larger Moths of Surrey by Graham A. Collins
". . . a much-needed, thorough and extremely well-researched book." – ATROPOS

Hoverflies of Surrey by Roger K. A. Morris
"It should be, as the publishers hope, a model of its kind." – BRITISH WILDLIFE

Grasshoppers and Crickets of Surrey by David W. Baldock
". . . without doubt, the best County Orthoptera to be published to date."
– BIOLOGICAL RECORDS CENTRE ORTHOPTERA RECORDING SCHEME

Ladybirds of Surrey by Roger D. Hawkins
*". . . an excellent book, a mine of information, attractively produced, and
easy to read."* – ANTENNA

Amphibians and Reptiles of Surrey by Julia Wycherley and Richard Anstis
". . . deserves a place on the shelf of any naturalist." – THE LONDON NATURALIST

Shieldbugs of Surrey by Roger D. Hawkins
*"Entomologists thinking of starting on the study of true bugs would be well
advised to start here . . . this is natural history at its best."*
– ENTOMOLOGIST'S MONTHLY MAGAZINE

Also published by Surrey Wildlife Trust

THE SURREY COUNTY CHECKLIST SERIES

1. The Beetles of Surrey – a Checklist by Dr Jonty Denton

**All titles can be ordered through bookshops, or via
Surrey Wildlife Trust's website: www.surreywildlifetrust.org**